ECONOMIES OF SCALE AND TECHNOLOGICAL CHANGE IN THERMAL POWER GENERATION

CONTRIBUTIONS
TO
ECONOMIC ANALYSIS

53

Edited by

J. JOHNSTON

J. SANDEE

R. H. STROTZ

J. TINBERGEN

P. J. VERDOORN

NORTH-HOLLAND PUBLISHING COMPANY

AMSTERDAM

ECONOMIES OF SCALE AND TECHNOLOGICAL CHANGE IN THERMAL POWER GENERATION

MALCOLM GALATIN

The City College of The City University of New York

1968

NORTH-HOLLAND PUBLISHING COMPANY

AMSTERDAM

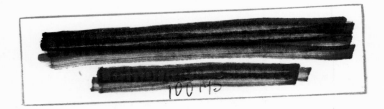

PRINTED IN THE NETHERLANDS

INTRODUCTION TO THE SERIES

This series consists of a number of hitherto unpublished studies, which are introduced by the editors in the belief that they represent fresh contributions to economic science.

The term *economic analysis* as used in the title of the series has been adopted because it covers both the activities of the theoretical economist and the research worker.

Although the analytical methods used by the various contributors are not the same, they are nevertheless conditioned by the common origin of their studies, namely theoretical problems encountered in practical research. Since for this reason, business cycle research and national accounting, research work on behalf of economic policy, and problems of planning are the main sources of the subjects dealt with, they necessarily determine the manner of approach adopted by the authors. Their methods tend to be "practical" in the sense of not being too far remote from application to actual economic conditions. In addition they are quantitative rather than qualitative.

It is the hope of the editors that the publication of these studies will help to stimulate the exchange of scientific information and to reinforce international cooperation in the field of economics.

THE EDITORS

To the memory of my father
Charles Galatin
1907–1967

PREFACE

This book is a revised version of a study submitted to the Department of Economics at the Massachusetts Institute of Technology in 1965. I am indebted to Professors Robert M. Solow, Franklin M. Fisher and Paul W. MacAvoy for their constructive criticisms and encouragement. My fellow graduate students at M.I.T. helped to provide an atmosphere which was as pleasant as it was stimulating. In the course of revision I have benefited from discussions with several of my colleagues at the University of Western Ontario, especially Professor Willem Somermeyer, now at the Econometric Institute of the Netherlands School of Economics. I am also grateful to Professor Jack Johnston for reading this book in manuscript form. Nevertheless, I am responsible for any errors which remain.

London, Ontario   M. GALATIN
May 1967

CONTENTS

10

LIST OF TABLES

CHAPTER 1

INTRODUCTION

The major problem considered in this book is how the effect of economies
of scale and technological change may be separated and quantified in a
production process, when the form of analysis is in micro- rather than
macro-terms. It is our opinion that although such an analysis in macro-
terms is both useful and relevant, the level of aggregation employed
necessarily makes any precise interpretation of the results obtained very
difficult. Further, the diverse nature of production processes in a complex
economy implies that the application of conventional production theory,
without the introduction of specific modifications suited to the production process in a particular sector, may lead to serious errors of analysis.
For this reason we consider a particular production model, the "multi-
unit plant", which adequately represents the production process in steam-
electric power generation, the industry which is considered in this study.

The problem of evaluating capital is avoided by identifying the capital
in a plant as a set of machines each of which is characterised by measures
of size and vintage, rather than by estimating some monetary aggregate.
The individual machine and the plant are the micro-units at which the
level of analysis proceeds. The composition of machines in a plant, its
"machine-mix", and the varied degrees of capacity utilisation of machines
are considered throughout the analysis.

In chapter 2 the reasons for the development of an alternative plant
model are given. The model of the multi-unit plant developed there has
both *ex-ante* and *ex-post* elements. The meaning of economies of scale and
technological change for such a model is given and related to economies of
scale and technological change in the conventional production model. In
an appendix to this chapter the long-run cost curves for the multi-unit
plant are derived.

Chapter 3 applies certain of the ideas of chapter 2 for the steam-electric
generating plant which is the multi-unit plant used for the empirical work

in this study. A simple model of electricity production is developed and certain measures of input and capacity utilisation are derived for individual machines in the steam-electric plant. In an appendix to this chapter the optimal use of a multi-unit plant is discussed.

Chapter 4 is a survey and critique of the literature on the estimation of production and cost functions for steam-electric power generation in the United States and the United Kingdom. It is shown that substantial criticisms may be made of these studies in terms of both the methodology adopted by the various authors and the methodology employed in this book. Two of the studies considered explicitly assumed cost-minimisation behaviour by plant managers in order to derive cost functions. It is shown that the form of cost-minimisation behaviour relevant to the steam-electric power industry is different from that assumed in these studies and hence incorrect cost functions have been specified and estimated. A discussion of the estimation of cost functions in an industry which has a capital stock lasting many years and where output may vary over the lifetime of the capital stock, is related to these various attempts at cost function estimation.

In chapter 5 we present the results of an estimation of the ex-post production functions (fuel input functions) for the steam-electric power industry of the United States. Particular forms of the ex-post production functions are used, which as well as making economic sense have desirable aggregation properties. It is shown that the aggregation problem considered here relates to the use of annual data to estimate the parameters of an essentially instantaneous production process. From these estimated functions the effects of changes in scale and technology are separated and quantified.

In chapter 6 capital- and labour-input functions are estimated. From these the effects of changes in scale and technology on capital costs and labour input are measured. The influence of machine-mix is explicitly considered. However the availability and quality of the capital and labour data means that this analysis is less satisfactory and comprehensive than that of the ex-post production function.

Chapter 7 brings together the results of chapters 5 and 6 in illustrative examples of cost calculations for steam-electric plants. A simplified form of the investment decision of the plant operator is also considered.

Finally, in chapter 8 our conclusions are presented.

CHAPTER 2

THE MULTI-UNIT PLANT MODEL: RETURNS TO SCALE AND TECHNOLOGICAL CHANGE

2.1. Introduction

In this chapter we discuss a model of the production process for those activities where the flow of capital services is provided by a stock of capital which is not divisible, and such that the machines or units which make up the capital stock differ in terms of size and vintage. It will be shown that a conventional production function does not adequately describe these processes, and that this new model allows us to derive measures of, and differentiate between, the effects of changes in scale and technology.

2.2. The production process in a multi-unit plant

Conventional production theory is based on the concept of a production function which specifies the maximum output Q, obtainable from inputs of capital K, and m variable inputs X_i, $i = 1, ..., m$. This function is shown in equation (2.1).

$$Q = F(K, X_1, X_2, ..., X_m). \qquad (2.1)$$

The variables in (2.1) should all relate to the same time period but we omit time subscripts for convenience. The domain of application of (2.1) may be the plant, the firm, the industry, or the total economy. We shall be interested in the production process at the level of the individual plant.

In (2.1), all the inputs and the output are assumed to be homogeneous and divisible. There are, however, many production processes where the assumption of a homogeneous and divisible input K, does not reflect the

17

true nature of capital in the production process. For example, the aircraft used in transportation, the equipment used in manufactured gas and sugar refining and the turbines used in steam-electric power generation differ in terms of capacity size and vintage. Thus in many activities the units of capital which provide capital services as an input are neither homogeneous nor divisible, and we cannot in principle measure these capital services by one aggregate K,[1] without ignoring several important dimensions of capital in the production process.

For example, consider that the desired output from a plant in a time period is $\bar{Q}$. Then there are numerous capital stocks that could provide this output, e.g., one machine of size[2] $\bar{Q}$, two of size 0.5 $\bar{Q}$, two of size $\bar{Q}$ each working at 50 per cent of capacity, and so on. Thus the input of capital services required to produce any specific output may be derived from a multitude of different sizes of machines in the plant which differ in terms of size and which may or may not be operated at full capacity in the time period.[3] The possible number of machine-mixes increases when machines may also differ in terms of vintage, i.e., the extent to which technological change is embodied in the machine.

There have been some attempts to measure capital allowing for hetero-

---

[1] In the fitting of production functions the estimation of capital is the greatest difficulty. Although a distinction is made in theory between the stock of capital and the capital services provided by that stock in a time period, in practice estimates of the capital stock are used in fitting production functions. Thus for the purposes of empirical work the assumption of a homogeneous and divisible capital stock which is used as a proxy for capital services greatly violates the true nature of capital in many activities. See also footnote 4 and footnote 5, where some attempts to modify capital estimates to allow for heterogeneity and the degree of capacity utilisation, are discussed.

[2] As will be discussed below, p. 20, "size" means the maximum output of the machine in the time period.

[3] It may be objected that if we are interested in measuring capital services, there will be a unique quantity of capital services which together with a fixed vector of variable input quantities produces any specified output, no matter what the machine-mix of the capital stock which provides these services is. But since in practice estimates of the stock of capital (in money terms) are used as a proxy for capital services, there is no reason why only one machine-mix would produce a specified output with a fixed vector of variable inputs. Thus there is no unique K that may be measured along the capital axis (this is so even if machines are assumed to be of the same vintage). Any attempt to measure capital services directly for the heterogeneous capital plant soon leads to circular reasoning where we are measuring capital in terms of output!

geneity in terms of vintage,[4] and also the degree of capacity utilisation[5] has been introduced into estimated production functions. But the three dimensions of capital services resulting from differences in machine-mix in terms of size and vintage and differing degrees of capacity utilisation of machines have not been considered together in an attempt to measure an aggregate K which could be used in a conventional production function of the form (2.1).

In order to avoid the traps involved in attempting to measure capital, we need an alternative production model which avoids the problem by identifying rather than by attempting to measure capital.

We shall be interested in plants where a homogeneous output is produced on identifiable units of capital which we shall call "machines". Each machine uses inputs of labour and other variable inputs to produce the homogeneous output. Thus this plant model must be distinguished from one where different components of the final output are produced on different machines. We shall call our model the "multi-unit plant".

Schematically we may write the production function as follows:

$$Q_i = F_i(X_1, X_2, ..., X_m) \,|\, [Q_{Ki}, V_i], \quad i = 1, ..., N, \qquad (2.2)$$

---

[4] See R. M. SOLOW, Investment and Technical Progress, *Mathematical Methods in the Social Sciences*, Stanford: Stanford University Press, 1959, pp. 89–104. Solow shows that it is possible under certain circumstances to derive a single measure for a capital stock which is heterogeneous in terms of vintage; such that this measure may be used in a neo-classical production function.

[5] This has been done by either adjusting a stock measure of capital directly to obtain a flow measure or by introducing a utilisation variable. An example of the first method is the measure of capital used by Dhrymes and Kurz (see chapter 4, p. 84) which is not quite correct. Robin Marris in his work, *The Economics of Capital Utilisation* (footnote 1, p. 6), provides an example of the second method. He suggests a function

$$O = \lambda H^h E^e C^c$$

where O is annual output, H is utilisation measured in operating hours per year, E is instantaneous employment and C is capital measured at cost. Marris' H represents the degree of capacity operation over a year if it is assumed that output is at the maximum rate possible in each hour of operation. If this is not the case then it is difficult to see what H measures exactly. (See chapter 3, for a discussion of capacity utilisation in steam-electric generation.)

where Q_i is the maximum output forthcoming from m variable inputs $X_1, ..., X_m$ to the ith machine in a specific time period. The ith machine is characterised by a capacity measure Q_{Ki} and by a vintage index V_i. Q_{Ki} measures the maximum possible output obtainable on the machine in the time period and will alternatively be called the size (or capacity size) of the machine. V_i is an index which indicates the degree of technological know-ledge embodied in the machine.

If there are N different types of machine, each identified by a pair $[Q_{Ki}, V_i]$, then the set of N functions (2.2) is the set of blueprints available to an entrepreneur from which he must choose a machine-mix in order to build a plant. We shall call the N functions (2.2), the ex-ante production function.[6]

Once a machine is put in place the substitution possibilities between the variable inputs to produce output is given by the ex-post production function [7] which for the ith machine is:

$$Q_i = F_i(X_1, ..., X_m). \qquad (2.3)$$

Q_i cannot be greater than Q_{Ki}.

The properties of the ex-post production function (2.3) are similar to those of the conventional production function which includes capital as a variable input,[8] but the capacity constraints on the machine must be explicitly introduced. If there are only two variable inputs to a machine, then the substitution possibilities may be shown on an isoquant map as in figure 2.1.

The maximum output possible on the machine is $Q_K = Q_6$, but this will be achieved only if inputs are combined in the proportion given by the slope of Oa. If inputs are combined in any other proportion, then maximum output will be at the point of intersection of the ray from the origin with

---

[6] Compare with the treatment of capital in P. A. SAMUELSON, Parable and Realism in Capital Theory: The Surrogate Production Function, *The Review of Economic Studies*, XXIX(3), June 1962, p. 193.

[7] Compare with the view of capital adopted by R. M. SOLOW in Substitution and Fixed Proportions in the Theory of Capital, *ibid.*, p. 207, and by LEIF JOHANSEN in Substitution Versus Fixed Proportion Coefficients in the Theory of Economic Growth: A Synthesis, *Econometrica*, XXVII, April 1959, p. 157.

[8] In the Marshallian "long run".

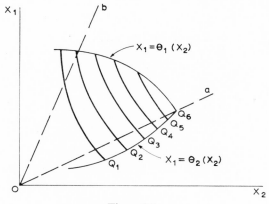

Figure 2.1.

slope equal to the factor proportions and a capacity constraint curve of the form $X_1 = \theta_1(X_2)$ or $X_1 = \theta_2(X_2)$.[9] For example, if variable factors are combined in the proportion given by the slope of Ob, then the greatest output in the time period is Q_2. There may not in practice be substitution possibilities ex-post between variable factors, but for any ex-post production function the maximum possible output whatever the proportions in which factors are combined will be called the size of the machine. Thus the machine of figure 2.1 has size $Q_K = Q_6$.

Finally we shall need the total variable cost function for a machine. For the case of two variable inputs the total variable (or ex-post) cost function is derived by minimising

$$C = P_1 X_1 + P_2 X_2, \tag{2.4}$$

subject to (a) $Q_i = F_i(X_1, X_2)$
  (b) $X_1 \leq \theta_1(X_2)$
  (c) $X_1 \geq \theta_2(X_2)$.

Unit factor costs P_1 and P_2 are assumed constant. The result of this cost minimising procedure enables us to derive the total variable cost function

$$C_i = C_i(Q_i, P_1, P_2) \tag{2.5}$$

for $Q_i \leq Q_{Ki}$

[9] These are analogous to the ridge lines of the conventional isoquant map.

which is the minimum total variable cost of producing an output of Q_i on the ith machine, which is of size Q_{Ki}. In a similar fashion the total variable cost function may be derived when there are m variable inputs.

To recapitulate: we have shown that for many production processes there is no adequate interpretation which may be given to a single variable indicating capital input in the production function. If we attempted to measure capital services by using a dollar measure of the capital stock as a proxy, then we would be ignoring differences in machine-mix and the degree of capacity utilisation of machines. In order to avoid these problems we have introduced a production model which identifies capital instead of attempting to measure it. We must now go on to consider the meaning of economies of scale in the multi-unit plant.

2.3.   Economies of scale in the multi-unit plant

Initially we shall consider the meaning of economies of scale when a conventional production function of the form (2.1) is assumed to adequately describe a production activity and then proceed to discuss the meaning of economies of scale in the multi-unit plant.

Two measures of economies of scale are discussed in the literature. The first may be called the "technical description", and the second is related to shape of the long-run average cost curve. First the technical description.[10] There are said to be increasing, constant, or decreasing returns to scale when the quotient Z, given by (2.6) is greater, equal to, or less than λ, when λ is a constant >1.

$$Z = \frac{F(\lambda K, \lambda L, \lambda X_1, ..., \lambda X_m)}{F(K, L, X_1, ..., X_m)}. \qquad (2.6)$$

The interpretation of (2.6) is as follows. Consider any point on the isoquant map in $m+1$ dimensional factor space. This is defined by the vector of inputs to the production function in the denominator on the right-

---

[10] For example, see SUNE CARLSON, *A Study on the Pure Theory of Production*, New York: A. M. Kelley, 1965, p. 17. Carlson's notation is different from ours, but his meaning is equivalent to the technical description used above.

hand side of (2.6). Assume now that we increase all inputs by the same proportion $(\lambda-1)$, then there are increasing, constant, or decreasing returns to scale as the proportionate increase in output is greater than, equal to, or less than $(\lambda-1)$. Thus returns to scale are defined at any point on the production function.

However we are interested in the effects of scale changes as the entrepreneur makes proportional variations in all inputs over the range of his long-run expansion path. By definition the technical description of economies of scale will only be defined between points on the isoquant map that lie on a line through the origin. Therefore if the long-run expansion path is not a straight line through the origin, input variations on this path will not be the result of equi-proportionate increases in all factor inputs, and the technical description of economies of scale will not apply to the full range of output points along the long-run expansion path. Only if the long-run expansion path is a line through the origin, will the technical description of economies of scale be meaningful for the potential levels of output of the plant or firm.[11]

In order to speak about economies of scale for outputs along the long-run expansion path a second approach has been used.[12] From the long-

---

[11] For example, if there are only two inputs and we consider scale effects between A and B which lie on the long-run expansion path, then the technical description of economies of scale is applicable between A and B' on Oa and between A' and B on Ob, but not between A and B.

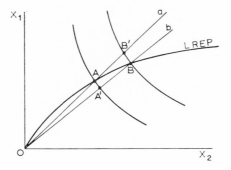

[12] For example, see C. E. FERGUSON, *Microeconomic Theory*, Homewood, Ill: Richard D. Irwin, Inc., 1966, pp. 180–183.

run expansion path the long-run average cost curve may be derived. Economies of scale have been related to the shape of long-run average costs. Thus, there are said to be increasing, constant, or decreasing returns to scale as long-run average costs are falling, constant, or increasing.

These two descriptions of economies of scale will only coincide when the long-run expansion path is a straight line. This will be the case when the production function (2.1) is homogeneous,[13] and there will be increasing, constant, or decreasing returns to scale as the production function is homogeneous of degree greater than, equal to, or less than unity. Similarly, long-run average costs will fall over the full output range when the production function is homogeneous of degree greater than one, be constant when it is linearly homogeneous, and rise over all outputs when homogeneity is less than one.

The distinction between the two indicators of economies of scale is increased when a non-divisible factor "management" is introduced to which is laid the blame for the upward sloping portion of the long-run average cost curve and hence diseconomies of scale.

Now we must proceed to consider measures of economies of scale in the multi-unit plant. First at the level of the individual machine we have an analogous measure which we call intra-capacity economies. We say that there are increasing, constant, or decreasing returns to capacity utilisation for the ith machine as Z_i, given by (2.7) is greater than, equal to, or smaller than λ, when λ is a constant > 1.

$$Z_i = \frac{F_i(\lambda X_1, \lambda X_2, \lambda X_3, ..., \lambda X_m)}{F_i(X_1, X_2, X_3, ..., X_m)} \qquad (2.7)$$

The relevant production function F_i, is the ex-post production function (2.3). Also the numerator on the right-hand side of (2.7) cannot be greater than the capacity output implied by the factor proportions in the denominator.[14]

---

[13] A sufficient but not necessary condition.

[14] We may also relate intra-capacity economies to the shape of the average variable cost function for the ith machine, and in line with the discussion above, p. 23, there is no necessity for a one-to-one relationship to exist between the two measures of intra-capacity economies.

When we consider the meaning of economies of scale at the plant level there is no analogy to the technical description of economies of scale given by (2.6), for as we have seen above there is no single variable K which may be used to measure the input of capital in a multi-unit plant.[15] Since this is the case, the only meaningful description of economies of scale in the multi-unit plant must be related to the shape of the long-run average cost (LRAC) curve for the plant. This will be of the form

$$\text{LRAC} = G(Q, p_1, p_2, ..., p_m, n_1(Q), n_2(Q), ..., n_N(Q), r_1, r_2, ..., r_N),$$
(2.8)

where Q is total plant output, r_i is the cost of the ith machine when there are N machines in the ex-ante production function, and p_j is the unit cost of the jth variable factor, $j = 1, ..., m$. The derivation of (2.8) is discussed in the appendix to this chapter.

Given (2.8) we may say that there are increasing, constant, or decreasing returns to scale as long-run average costs are falling, constant, or rising.

2.4. Technological change in the multi-unit plant

The analysis of economies of scale in the multi-unit plant assumed a constant ex-ante production function. Technological change becomes evident when there is a change in the ex-ante production function by the addition of blueprints, i.e., ex-post production possibilities. This embodied technological change may take several forms. There may be shifts in the ex-post production functions for machines of a given size when compared with machines of the same size but of earlier vintage. Machines of a larger size than previously could be built, may now be introduced. There may be changes in the nature of the variable inputs used. In addition, changes in techniques may be introduced by adding equipment to existing machines or altering them in some manner.

---

[15] To emphasize this point once again: the increase in capital services represented by $(\lambda - 1)K$ in (2.6), may result from various combinations of machine additions to the plant and/or variation in the degree of capacity utilization of machines in the plant.

For the plant as a whole, organisational changes may lead to greater output with no change in the inputs of variable factors or the machine-mix. This is the familiar disembodied technological change of neo-classical analysis.

Finally, a distinction should be made between virtual and actual, or ex-ante and ex-post, technological change. The addition of blueprints to the ex-ante production function implies virtual technological change which only becomes actual when new machines are put in place in a plant.[16]

2.5. The empirical analysis in relation to the theory

All econometric analysis is based on an approximation to an underlying theoretical structure. In the measurement of economies of scale and technological change in the steam-electric power generating industry of the United States,[17] we have taken the multi-unit plant model as the basis for our estimates. The measurements of economies of scale are derived by comparing the ex-post production functions for individual machines of different sizes, but of the same vintage. The effects of technological change are measured by looking at the shift of the ex-post production function for machines of the same size, but of different vintage. The same method is applied to capital- and labour-input functions for the plant as a whole. Our device of identifying rather than measuring capital will enable us to differentiate between these effects of changes of scale and technology.

Appendix

The long-run average cost function for the multi-unit plant

The analysis proceeds in two steps. First we shall consider the optimal

---

[16] This is not the same as the difference between invention and innovation.
[17] Chapters 5 and 6.

use of a plant with a fixed machine-mix which enables us to derive short-run cost functions, and the second step is to consider the optimal composition of a plant when the entrepreneur has the opportunity to change the machine-mix, i.e., the long-run situation.

In the short-run it is assumed that a plant has a fixed machine-mix of n_i machines of type i where $i = 1, ..., N$. The total variable cost function for the ith machine is given by $C_i = C_i(Q_i, p_1, ..., p_m)$,[18] and Q_{Ki} is the maximum capacity on the machine. Then the short-run total variable cost function (TVC) is the locus of minimum costs for each plant output Q, where

$$0 \leq Q \leq \sum_{i=1}^{N} n_i Q_{Ki}.$$

We proceed as follows. For any output Q, divide this output among the machines in the plant such that total variable cost is minimised. Formally we have to solve the following programming problem, find a set of numbers Q_{ij} such that,

$$C = \sum_{i=1}^{N} \sum_{j=1}^{n_i} C_{ij}[Q_{ij}, p_1, p_2, ..., p_m] \qquad (2.9)$$

is minimised, subject to

(a) $Q_{ij} \leq Q_{Ki}$ $i = 1, ..., N$

(b) $\sum_{i=1}^{N} \sum_{j=1}^{n_i} Q_{ij} = Q$ $j = 1, ..., n_i$

(c) $\sum_{i=1}^{N} n_i Q_{Ki} \geq Q$

(d) $Q_{ij} \geq 0$

where Q_{ij} is output on the jth machine of type i. $C_{ij}(Q_{ij}, p_1, ..., p_m)$ is the total variable cost function for the jth machine of type i, which will of course be the same for all machines of type i.[19]

---

[18] See equation (2.5).
[19] See the appendix to chapter 3, where the solution to this problem is obtained for a plant with a specific machine-mix.

The solution of this programming problem enables us to derive the TVC function for the plant which will be of the form

$$\text{TVC} = H(Q, p_1, p_2, ..., p_m) \,|\, (n_1, n_2, ..., n_N). \tag{2.10}$$

The interpretation of (2.10) is the minimum TVC of producing an output Q in a plant with a fixed machine-mix given by the vector $(n_1, n_2, ..., n_N)$. To derive the short-run total cost (SRTC) function of the plant we simply have to add total fixed costs to TVC and we derive

$$\text{SRTC} = \left[H(Q, p_1, p_2, ..., p_m) + \sum_{i=1}^{N} r_i n_i \right] \Big| (n_1, ..., n_N) \tag{2.11}$$

where r_i is the cost of the ith machine.[20]

The long-run total cost (LRTC) function is derived in an analogous fashion to the LRTC function of conventional theory. It is simply the envelope to the set of SRTC functions (where there is an SRTC function for each machine-mix chosen from the ex-ante production function).

Formally the LRTC function is derived in the following manner. Suppose the desired plant output is Q; then the long-run minimum cost of producing Q is obtained by choosing the smallest total cost of producing Q from (2.11) for all feasible choices of machine-mix. Therefore

$$\text{LRTC}(Q) = \min_{(n_1, n_2 ..., n_N)} \left\{ \left[H(Q, p_1, ..., p_m) + \sum_{i=1}^{N} r_i n_i \right] \Big| (n_1, ..., n_N) \right\} \tag{2.12}$$

where the minimisation procedure is over all feasible machine-mixes $(n_1, ..., n_N)$.[21] Hence we may write the LRTC function for the plant in the

---

[20] It is possible that there will be economies of scale in terms of capital cost due to special discounts and saving in the cost of ancillary equipment (see chapter 6). Thus total fixed cost may be more accurately expressed as $C_{FC}(n_1, n_2, ..., n_N, r_1, r_2, ..., r_N)$.

[21] Where a feasible machine-mix, $(n_1, n_2, ..., n_N)$, is one such that,

$$\sum_{i=1}^{N} Q_{Ki} n_i \geq Q.$$

alternative form,

$$\text{LRTC} = G\left(Q, p_1, p_2, ..., p_m, n_1(Q), n_2(Q) ..., n_N(Q), r_1, r_2, ..., r_N\right) \tag{2.13}$$

where the number of machines of each type used in a long-run situation will depend on the level of plant output, Q.[22]

From (2.13) the long-run average cost and marginal cost functions may be derived as follows:

$$\text{LRAC} = \frac{\text{LRTC}}{Q} \tag{2.14}$$

$$\text{LRMC} = \frac{\partial}{\partial Q} \text{LRTC}. \tag{2.15}$$

The shape of the long-run average cost function (2.14) may be used as an indicator of economies of scale in the multi-unit plant as is discussed, p. 25, above.

---

[22] The LRTC function for the multi-unit plant plays the same role as the LRTC function for the homogeneous K plant. In both cases it is a planning device which gives the optimum capital input for a one-period optimisation procedure. For the homogeneous K plant the optimum quantity of capital is given by the LRTC function for any choice of output, while for the multi-unit plant the optimal machine-mix is given.

CHAPTER 3

THE STEAM-ELECTRIC GENERATING PLANT VIEWED AS A MULTI-UNIT PLANT: MEASURES OF CAPACITY UTILISATION AND FUEL INPUT OF INDIVIDUAL MACHINES

3.1. Introduction

In this chapter and those which follow we shall be concerned with an empirical application of certain of the ideas expressed in chapter 2 regarding the production process in a multi-unit plant. The example chosen is that of the steam-electric generating industry in the United States. Data on inputs and outputs for this industry are available on a plant-by-plant basis, and it is virtually unique in this respect.[1] Because of the availability of such data several studies have been made of this industry in an attempt to give empirical content to the meaning of returns to scale and technological change at the level of micro-economic analysis. Both production and cost functions have been estimated. Sufficient justification for a further empirical study is based on criticisms of the models that have been used, in terms of their reflection of the actual production process, the statistical techniques employed and the measurement of important variables.[2]

This chapter sets out a simple model of the ex-post production function for steam-electric power which enables important variables to be determined from the published statistics. In an appendix to this chapter the problem of using a multi-unit plant optimally, in the sense of minimising total variable cost of an exogenously determined output, is discussed.

---

[1] The source of data is the series *Steam-Electric Plant Construction Cost and Annual Production Expenses*, published by the Federal Power Commission and hereafter referred to as the FPC Reports.

[2] See chapter 4.

3.2.   The steam-electric plant viewed as a multi-unit plant

We shall be concerned with the production of power in steam-electric plants which use fossilized fuels, coal, oil and natural gas. In 1964 these thermal plants accounted for more than 80 per cent of the total generation of electricity in the United States. By 1980 this proportion is expected to fall to 68 per cent [3] but the absolute increase in steam-electric power generation will be of the order of 200 per cent. [4] The remaining portion of electricity generation is derived from hydro-electric and nuclear power plants with which we shall not be concerned in this study.

In 1963 some 514 steam-electric plants in the United States accounted for 88 per cent of installed capacity and 94 per cent of total output of steam plants. [5] There is a wide range in the size and vintage of units installed in these plants. In general a plant may be composed of units of different sizes and vintages, although in many cases both size and vintage will be uniform for all units in a plant. Thus the steam-electric plant may be viewed as a multi-unit plant, in which a homogeneous, non-storable product, electricity, is produced on a variety of machines of different size and vintage.

These machines are the turbine-generator units with their associated system of boilers. For this study the machine will be identified as the turbine generator. The assumption will be made that at the time when a turbine is installed the most efficient system of boilers and ancillary equipment is put in place with that turbine. [6] Thus changes in scale and

---

[3] The Federal Power Commission, *The National Power Survey, 1964*. Washington: Government Printing Office, 1964, p. 63.

[4] *Ibid.*, pp. 27 and 39. U.S. 1960 actual output 761 billion kWh; 1980 projected 2693 billion kWh. In 1960 the per cent derived from fossilised fuels was 81, in 1980 projected 68 per cent. Thus these data imply the 200 per cent absolute increase in output of 1980 over 1960.

[5] *FPC Report 1962–1963*, p. i.

[6] The "most efficient" system of boilers and ancillary equipment is determined by the optimal investment programme. When the machine is composed of a number of units the only means of identifying the vintage and size is to consider one part of it as is done here. Boiler design and technique progressed somewhat independently of turbine technology. "The increase in sizes of turbines however (after 1900) was not immediately accompanied by an increase in the size of boilers. At first a battery of several boilers was necessary to supply the steam required for one turbine, but major improvements

technology will be identified with changes in the size and vintage of the
turbine and it will be assumed that the necessary adjustment in scale and
technology of boilers and other ancillary equipment was made.

The unit of observation in this study is the machine, rather than the
plant or the firm. The justification for this is that we are concerned with a
production process where the basic unit of capital is the machine. The
measurement and separation of the effects of changes in technology and
scale is then best understood by relating them to a readily identifiable
unit – the turbine generator. Also, in terms of the investment decision of
a utility, once a plant size is determined for a particular locality, the choice
of machine-mix for the plant will depend on the operating characteristics
and costs of available machines. [7]

Each machine, when in place, uses inputs of variable factors, fuel,
labour and water, to produce electricity. It will be shown (chapter 6) that
labour is virtually a fixed factor. Fuel cost dominates variable cost and in
this study fuel is considered as the only variable input in terms of the
ex-post production function. Some machines can only use one type of
fuel and the investment costs and input functions will be shown to vary
as the type of fuel used. [8] It is possible for an additional investment to add
special burners to a machine that enable coal, oil or natural gas to be
used depending on the availability and delivered cost of such fuel. Rather
than distinguishing between the physical quantities of different fuel inputs
the calorific content of fuel, measured in terms of British Thermal Units,
will be used.

The ex-post production process is virtually instantaneous. Each turbine
has a certain name-plate rating, designated by the producer of the unit,
which denotes in principle the maximum instantaneous production
capability of that machine measured in megawatts (thousand kilowatts)
of electricity. Thus the name-plate rating is in principle the maximum
instantaneous capacity or size of the machine in terms of physical output

---

followed in boiler design. Today's modern plants commonly have unit boiler-turbine-
generator combinations." (*National Power Survey 1964*, Part I, p. 63).

[7] For a utility which supplies electricity as well as produces it and which may buy
electricity as well as sell it, the operating characteristics and costs of a machine are
only two of the variables it must take into account for its overall investment decision.

[8] See chapters 5 and 6.

units. In actual practice, however, the name-plate rating of a turbine generator is not an unambiguous measure of the instantaneous capacity and will vary depending on the exact specification of the cooling and pressure systems of the machine. Changes in these specifications lead to a rerating of the name-plate capacity of machines.[9] Incorrect specification of instantaneous capacity can enable units to operate at more than 100 per cent of capacity as calculated on the basis of published name-plate ratings.

In general the most recent name-plate rating of a turbine was accepted as a measure of its instantaneous capacity, despite its shortcomings, for there is no obvious alternative method of obtaining a measure of physical capacity.

3.3. A model of electricity generation

We shall now consider a more formal model of electricity production. This will enable measures of the degree of capacity utilisation and fuel input for individual machines to be derived from the data published by the FPC for plants as a whole. A major criticism of previous studies of steam-electric power generation is that in some cases no allowance has been made for the degree of capacity utilisation of machines. Where this has been explicitly considered, the measure used is incorrect.[10]

Ex-post, fuel is the only variable input used on a machine of name-plate rating, X_K, the instantaneous capacity output. The maximum generation possible in the unit time interval, dt, is $X_K dt$. The machine, however, may be operated at less than the capacity rate; the actual output in the unit interval is $X_t dt$, where $0 \leq X_t \leq X_K$. Fuel input is measured in British Thermal Units per kilowatt/dt and is denoted by a_t. a_t is not a constant but will be a function of the size and degree of capacity utilisation of the

---

[9] See the *FPC Report 1962–63*, p. ii, where it is shown that the increase in capacity due to a rerating of turbine generators from 1957 to 1963 was 8886 megawatts. This represents some 15.2 per cent of the net increase in installed capacity in steam-electric plants from 1957 to 1963 (*ibid*. Table 2, p. xix, where total installed capacity is recorded). However, the extent of rerating for earlier years (including the period covered by the sample in this study) was less significant.
[10] See chapter 4.

machine in the unit period. Thus

$$a_t = g\left(X_t/X_K; X_K\right) \tag{3.1}$$

where X_t/X_K is the level of capacity utilisation in the unit period. The function g, will also depend on the vintage of the machine, but for now we shall not be concerned with technological change. (3.1) is simply the ex-post production function[11] and we may postulate that

$$\frac{\partial g}{\partial\left(X_t/X_K\right)} < 0;\ \frac{\partial^2 g}{\partial\left(X_t/X_K\right)^2} > 0 \tag{3.2}$$

which gives rise to a function shown in figure 3.1.

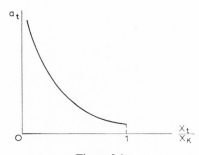

Figure 3.1.

From (3.1) we may derive,

$$f_t = h\left(X_t/X_K; X_K\right) \tag{3.3}$$

where f_t is the total fuel input in the unit time interval which depends on the vintage[12] and size $\left(X_K\right)$ of the machine, and the degree of capacity $\left(X_t/X_K\right)$ used. Condition (3.2) implies that

$$\frac{\partial^2 h}{\partial\left(X_t/X_K\right)^2} < 0 \tag{3.4}$$

---

[11] Equation (3.1) is really a transform of the ex-post production function but it will be called the ex-post production function in this study.

[12] Which affects the value of the parameters and perhaps the functional form of h.

and the fuel-input function (3.3) is shown in figure 3.2. However there is a problem here, for the function h is not single valued when $X_t/X_K=0$. This is due to the nature of the production process and we must consider the utilisation of a turbine in a unit period dt.

A machine may or may not be operated during the interval dt. Let dt_1 indicate that a machine is said to be "hot and connected to load" in the unit interval. This means that the machine is burning fuel and producing electricity. dt_2 indicates that in the unit time interval the machine is said to be "hot but not connected to load". In this situation, boilers are kept hot, there is some fuel input, but the turbine is not actively operating, even though it is spinning, and no electricity is being produced. The reason for maintaining a machine in this condition is that due to the un-even spread of load over the hours of a day, at certain times not all units

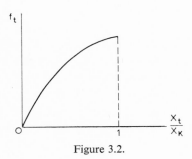

Figure 3.2.

in a plant will be operating. With a complicated machine it may pay to keep the turbine hot but not connected to load rather than stop the firing of boilers with the necessity of relighting boilers when the machine is needed to produce. A turbine-generator set that is hot but not connected to load can quickly be connected and produce electricity.

The third description of the operation of a machine is when it is "held in cold reserve" during the time interval. No fuel is burned, no electricity is generated and the boilers have to be refired before any production can take place. dt_3 will be used to signify that a machine is not operating in this sense.

Thus the fuel-input function (3.3) must be modified to take into account these different states of a machine in the unit time interval. This is done in

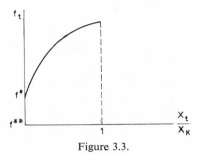

Figure 3.3.

figure 3.3 where f^* is fuel input for dt_2 and f^{**} is fuel input for a unit period of type dt_3.

There is no data for the instantaneous production process apart from a measure of X_K. In general data for a plant as a whole are published for T-unit periods which are divided into three intervals: t_1, when the plant is hot and connected to load; t_2, when it is hot but not connected to load; and t_3, when it is held in cold reserve. The problem then arises of how to determine appropriate measures of the degree of capacity utilisation and fuel input for individual machines in the plant over the time period T. It is shown below[13] how these measures over a discrete period T may be used to estimate the parameters of the essentially instantaneous production process (3.1). First we shall consider the measure of the degree of capacity utilisation of machines.

3.4. The measure of capacity utilisation

Total output for a machine over the period T is given by[14]

$$G = \int_{t=0}^{t=t_1} X_t dt.$$ (3.5)

---

[13] Chapter 5.

[14] For ease of notation the first t_1 unit periods of T are taken as being the periods when the plant operates hot and connected to load. But the analysis in no way depends on this.

Maximum output possible over T is

$$G_{max} = \int_{t=0}^{t=T} X_K dt.$$ (3.5a)

A reasonable measure of capacity utilisation is then given by

$$C_1 = \frac{G}{G_{max}}$$ (3.6)

which is the ratio of actual output to the maximum possible output over T. This measure is relevant if the degree of spare capacity in the machine is the desired variable, but for the production process what is needed is the degree to which the machine was utilised in relation to capacity during its period of actual output. A more relevant measure of capacity utilisation is given by

$$C_2 = \frac{1}{t_1} \int_0^{t_1} \frac{X_t}{X_K} dt = \frac{\int_0^{t_1} X_t dt}{t_1 X_K} = \frac{G}{t_1 X_K},$$ (3.7)

which is simply the arithmetic mean of the instantaneous degrees of capacity utilisation over the period when the machine is operated hot and connected to load. It may also be interpreted as the ratio of actual output to maximum possible output over the period when the machine is actually producing $(t_1 \le T)$. $C_1 \le C_2$, so that a measure of the degree of capacity utilisation over T which does not take into account the fact that in some intervals the machine will not be producing, underestimates the degree of capacity utilisation (unless $t_1 = T$).

In general, however, the plant has a machine-mix of different sizes and vintages such that the ith machine of capacity X_{K_i} will operate for a period t_{1i} hot and connected to load. The relevant measure of capacity utilisation analogous to (3.7) is given by

$$C_3 = \frac{\sum_{i=1}^{M} \int_0^{t_{1i}} X_{ti} dt_i}{\sum_{i=1}^{M} t_{1i} X_{K_i}}$$ (3.8)

where there are M machines in the plant and X_{ti} is the output of machine i at time t.

If plants are chosen such that all machines are of the same size the measure of capacity utilisation is

$$C_4 = \frac{\sum_{i=1}^{M} \int_0^{t_{1i}} X_{ti} dt_i}{X_K \sum_{i=1}^{M} t_{1i}}. \tag{3.9}$$

The variable C_4 is the theoretical measure of capacity utilisation for the plant as a whole; it is simply the ratio of actual output to maximum possible output over the period when machines are operated hot and connected to load.

In the published statistics the period of observation on a plant is a year. Thus T is 8760 hours and 8784 hours in a leap year. The unit period dt is taken to be an hour. Data are published for the plant as a whole giving values for t_1, t_2 and t_3 which are hours when the plant is hot and connected, hot but not connected, and cold, respectively. There is no differentiation between individual machines in the plant.

The published statistic which may be used to derive a measure of capacity utilisation is the plant factor (PF), which for a plant with only one machine is defined as

$$PF = \frac{\sum_{j=1}^{t_1} X_j}{T X_K} = \frac{\text{net generation}}{\text{hours in year} \times \text{name-plate rating}}. \tag{3.10}$$

The relevant measure of capacity utilisation C_2, may be directly derived from the data or by calculating

$$C_2 = PF^* = PF \cdot \frac{T}{t_1}. \tag{3.11}$$

Thus for a plant with only one unit the published plant factor underestimates the degree of capacity utilisation when $T > t_1$.

When the plant is composed of more than one unit the derivation of a measure of capacity utilisation for each machine in the plant is not so simple. For a plant composed of M machines of varying capacities, X_{K_i}, the published plant factor is given by

$$PF = \frac{\sum\limits_{i=1}^{M} \sum\limits_{j=1}^{t_{1i}} X_{ij}}{T \sum\limits_{i=1}^{M} X_{K_i}} \qquad (3.12)$$

where X_{ij} is the output of the ith machine during its jth hour of operating hot and connected to load. The corrected measure of capacity utilisation, allowing for the fact that the plant does not operate hot and connected for every hour in the year, is from (3.8)

$$C_3 = PF^* = PF \cdot \frac{T \sum\limits_{i=1}^{M} X_{Ki}}{\sum\limits_{i=1}^{M} t_{1i} X_{Ki}}. \qquad (3.13)$$

There is no way of calculating PF* directly or adjusting the published PF, for the t_{1i}, the hours hot and connected for each machine, are not published. It is seen that as for the plant with a single machine, the PF for a multi-unit plant is an underestimate of the degree of capacity utilisation unless $t_{1i} = T$ for each machine. The published t_1 for the plant as a whole allows no distinction to be made for the operating time of different machines. In general the individual hours of operation hot and connected for each machine will be smaller than the hours when at least one machine is operated hot and connected which is the published t_1. In order to obtain a measure of capacity utilisation, however, it is necessary to assume that each machine is operated for t_1 hours. Thus for the plant as a whole the measure of capacity utilisation is given by

$$PF^* = PF \cdot \frac{T \sum\limits_{i=1}^{M} X_{Ki}}{t_1 \sum\limits_{i=1}^{M} X_{Ki}} = PF \cdot \frac{T}{t_1}. \qquad (3.14)$$

This will be an underestimate of the correct measure of capacity utilisation given by (3.13).[15]

The sample of plants is chosen so that each machine in a plant is of the same size and vintage. For such plants the assumption that each machine operates for the same number of hours hot and connected is more plausible than for plants composed of a machine-mix of units of different size and vintage where older and smaller machines may only be used for peaking purposes. For these plants the measure of capacity utilisation may easily be calculated directly from (3.14) or from

$$\text{PF}^* = \frac{\displaystyle\sum_{i=1}^{M}\sum_{j=1}^{t_{1i}} X_{ij}}{t_1 \cdot M \cdot X_K} = \frac{\text{output}}{\text{hours hot and connected} \times \text{number of} \atop \text{machines} \times \text{capacity of each machine}}. \tag{3.15}$$

The problem now arises of how to determine the degree of capacity utilisation of each machine from this measure for the plant as a whole. If it is assumed that the output on each machine is the same over the year then (3.15) becomes,

$$\text{PF}^* = \frac{M \displaystyle\sum_{j=1}^{t_1} X_j}{t_1 \cdot M \cdot X_K} = \frac{\displaystyle\sum_{j=1}^{t_1} X_j}{t_1 X_K} \tag{3.16}$$

which is equivalent to C_2 of equation (3.7). Thus the calculated PF* from (3.15) may be taken as the measure of capacity utilisation for each individual machine in the plant. It is important to note that the two assumptions that have been made to derive a measure of the degree of capacity utilisation for each machine, i.e. (i) that each machine operates for t_1 hours hot and connected, and (ii) that the output on each machine over 8760 hours is the same, does not imply that each machine is operated at the same output rate at each hour. If each machine did operate at the same output rate at each hour then in (3.15) the X_{ij} would be the same for each machine and (3.15) would reduce to (3.16). It is more plausible for plants composed of units of the same size and vintage to assume that

---

[15] See Appendix D, p. 181, where the implications of this underestimation are further explored and related to the analysis of the appendix of this chapter and of chapter 5.

over the year the total output on each machine is the same. This problem, of the operation of a multi-unit plant, is more fully explored in the appendix to this chapter.

An appropriate measure of the degree of capacity utilisation for individual machines in the plant has now been derived. This is a necessary variable for the estimation of the ex-post production function (3.1). It is now required to derive the measure of fuel input from the published data.

3.5.   The measure of fuel input

The problem arises of deriving a measure of fuel input for each individual machine from data for plants as a whole on the basis of observations over $T = 8760$ hours. It is shown in chapter 5 that the theoretical measure of fuel input necessary for obtaining the parameters of the ex-post production function (3.1) is given by

$$B^* = \frac{\sum\limits_{j=1}^{t_1} f_j}{\sum\limits_{j=1}^{t_1} X_j}. \tag{3.17}$$

B^* is the input of fuel per unit of output for one machine over the period when the machine operates hot and connected to load. f_j and X_j are the input of fuel in BTU's and the output in kilowatts during the jth hour. Thus B^* is measured in BTU's per kilowatthour of generation.

The published statistic for the plant as a whole is given by

$$B = \frac{\sum\limits_{i=1}^{M} \sum\limits_{j=1}^{t_{1i}+t_{2i}} f_{ij}}{\sum\limits_{i=1}^{M} \sum\limits_{j=1}^{t_{1i}} X_{ij}} \tag{3.18}$$

where f_{ij} and X_{ij} are the input of fuel and the output of the ith machine during the jth hour. Thus in the published measure of fuel input no distinction is made between the time when the machine operates hot and connected to load and when it operates hot but not connected to load.

B may be partitioned in the following way,

$$B = \frac{\sum\limits_{i=1}^{M}\sum\limits_{j=1}^{t_{1i}} f_{ij}}{\sum\limits_{i=1}^{M}\sum\limits_{j=1}^{t_{1j}} X_{ij}} + \frac{\sum\limits_{i=1}^{M}\sum\limits_{j=1}^{t_{2i}} f_{ij}}{\sum\limits_{i=1}^{M}\sum\limits_{j=1}^{t_{1j}} X_{ij}} . \tag{3.19}$$

If the assumptions that were made to derive a measure of capacity utilisation are made here and in addition it is assumed that the total fuel input when the machine is operated hot and connected over the year is the same for each machine we have,

$$B = \frac{\sum\limits_{j=1}^{t_1} f_j}{\sum\limits_{j=1}^{t_1} X_j} + \frac{\sum\limits_{i=1}^{M}\sum\limits_{j=1}^{t_{2i}} f_{ij}}{\sum\limits_{i=1}^{M}\sum\limits_{j=1}^{t_{1j}} X_{ij}} . \tag{3.20}$$

The first term on the right-hand side of (3.20) is simply the desired variable B^* from (3.17). If the plants are restricted to those which have machines of the same size and vintage and it is assumed that each machine operates for the published t_2 hours hot but not connected we may write (3.20) in the form

$$B^* = B - \frac{M \cdot t_2 \cdot f^*}{\sum\limits_{i=1}^{M}\sum\limits_{j=1}^{t_{1j}} X_{ij}} \tag{3.21}$$

where f^* is the input of fuel per hour when the machine is operated hot but not connected to load. Since the sample is limited to plants where each machine has the same ex-post production function, f^* has the same value for each machine in the plant. This limitation of the sample makes the assumption that each machine operates for the same number of hours hot but not connected more plausible than if plants were considered which were composed of machines of varying vintage and capacity.

The problem now arises of how to adjust the published B for the fuel input when machines are hot but not connected to load. When a machine operates hot but not connected to load the input of fuel per hour necessary for keeping the boilers alight is a small proportion of the input of fuel per hour when the machine operates at full capacity. To be precise we shall take $f^* = 0.01 f_K$ where f_K is the input of fuel per hour in BTU's when the machine operates at full capacity.[16]

A precise measure of the fuel input per kilowatthour of net generation for each machine in the plant is then given by,

$$B^* = B - \frac{M \cdot t_2 \cdot 0.01 f_K}{\sum\limits_{i=1}^{M} \sum\limits_{j=1}^{t_{ij}} X_{ij}} \tag{3.22}$$

$$\therefore B^* = B - \frac{0.01 a_K}{\left(\dfrac{T}{t_2}\right) PF} \tag{3.23}$$

where a_K is the input of fuel per hour when the machine works at capacity i.e. f_K/X_K. B^* may be obtained from the published statistic B with a_K estimated from the fuel input per kilowatthour when the machine operates at the greatest observed degree of capacity utilisation.

---

[16] In private communication with the New England Power Company the following information was obtained concerning the banking charge for fuel (when the units are operated hot but not connected) compared with the fuel input when units are operated at full capacity.

Size of machine (in megawatts)	Fuel cost per hour (in dollars) when the machine is hot but not connected (1)	Fuel cost per hour (in dollars) at capacity (2)	(1)/(2)
50	1.7	195	0.87%
83	2.4	297	0.81%
150	3.9	495	0.79%

There is some indication that the fuel input when the machine is operated hot but not connected compared with the fuel input at full capacity operation falls as the size of unit increases. Also there is some variation for machines of different vintages. Thus the value taken for f^* is an approximation to the actual f^* on the basis of these figures. But as it will be shown in chapter 5 the adjustment procedure outlined here did not significantly affect the published values of B.

The problem of obtaining measures of input and capacity utilisation for each machine in a plant has now been solved. Further justification for the precise form of such measures adopted here, is given in the discussion of the problem of obtaining the parameters of (3.1) from annual data in chapter 5.

Appendix

The optimum utilisation of machines in the multi-unit plant

In order to derive measures of capacity utilisation and fuel input for individual machines in the plant, certain assumptions were made regarding output, fuel input and operating time on each machine over a year. An alternative assumption that could have been made, and is mentioned above (p. 41), is that each machine operates at the same output rate in each instant. This latter assumption is less plausible than the others as is seen from a consideration of the optimal operation of a multi-unit plant.

We shall only consider plants composed of machines of the same size and vintage. Each machine in a plant has, then, the same total variable cost function denoted by $C_i(X_i)$.[17] This function relates to a unit time interval. The subscript i simply identifies the machine in question when it is assumed there are M machines in the plant. X_i is output which must be less than or equal to capacity output X_K.

We shall consider the case where $C_i(X_i)$ has the following properties for all i:

$$\text{(i) } \frac{\partial C_i(X_i)}{\partial X_i} > 0 \qquad \text{(ii) } \frac{\partial^2 C_i(X_i)}{\partial X_i^2} < 0 \qquad (3.24)$$

$$\text{(iii) } C_i(0) = 0.$$

Thus the function C_i may be derived from the fuel-input function (3.3) above by multiplying f_t by the fuel price which is assumed constant. Condition (iii) implies that if the following analysis is applied to thermal electric plants the operation of a machine hot but not connected to load

---

[17] Factor prices are omitted here for simplicity.

is ignored. Since the fuel cost of a machine in this state is very small compared with fuel cost at capacity output (see footnote 17) the results obtained here may be applied without great error to thermal electric plants.

It is assumed that in each unit period a plant has to meet an exogenously determined demand. The optimum utilisation of machines in the plant is simply that division of output over machines which minimises total variable cost. The plant operator then is required to solve the following constrained minimisation problem:

To minimise $C = \sum_{i=1}^{M} C_i(X_i)$

subject to (a) $\sum_{i=1}^{M} X_i = \bar{X}$

(b) $0 \leq X_i \leq X_K \qquad i = 1, \ldots, M$

(3.25)

where C is total variable cost and $\bar{X}$ is the exogenously determined output for the unit period. For the total variable cost function having the properties (i), (ii) and (iii) above an explicit solution of this cost minimising problem may be obtained.

We shall first consider the solution to this problem for a plant consisting of two machines. Total variable costs are given by

$$C = C_1(X_1) + C_2(X_2).$$

(3.26)

Consider iso-cost curves such that for any values of X_1 and X_2 total variable cost C is constant. Then we have by taking the total derivative of (3.26) and holding C constant,

$$\frac{dX_1}{dX_2} = -\frac{\partial C_2(X_2)}{\partial X_2} \bigg/ \frac{\partial C_1(X_1)}{\partial X_1} = -\frac{MC_2}{MC_1}$$

(3.27)

where MC_i is the marginal cost of producing on machine i. Differentiating (3.27) with respect to X_2 we have

$$\frac{d^2X_1}{dX_2^2} = -\frac{\left[MC_1 \dfrac{\partial}{\partial X_2}(MC_2) + \dfrac{(MC_2)^2}{MC_1} \dfrac{\partial}{\partial X_1}(MC_1) \right]}{(MC_1)^2}.$$

(3.28)

From condition (ii) in (3.24) above, marginal cost is assumed to fall over
the full range of output on a machine, thus

$$\frac{d^2 X_1}{dX_2^2} > 0.$$
(3.29)

These iso-cost curves may be plotted on X_1, X_2 axes, figure 3.4, and will
be convex to the origin and of negative slope. Curves further away from

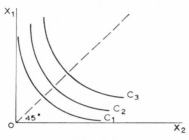

Figure 3.4.

the origin relate to successively greater total variable costs. These iso-cost
curves are also symmetrical about the 45° line through the origin, for if
any C is such that

$$C = C_1(X_1) + C_2(X_2)$$
(3.30)

is satisfied for $X_1 = a$, $X_2 = b$, the point $X_1 = b$, $X_2 = a$ also lies on this iso-
cost curve. From (3.27) the slope of the iso-cost curves on the 45° line
is -1.

Each of these iso-cost curves determines for any level of total variable
cost how output might be divided between the machines. It is now necessary to impose the capacity constraints (b) in (3.25) above on the diagram.
This is done in figure 3.5. The only feasible production points are those
on the boundary or inside the square $OX_K A X_K$ where X_K is the common
capacity of each machine. The solution to the constrained cost-minimisation problem (3.25) may now be derived and it is shown to depend on the
level of exogenous demand, $\bar{X} = X_1 + X_2$.

Case (i) $\qquad\qquad\qquad 0 \le X_1 + X_2 < X_K.$

For any output less than X_K the alternative combinations are given by
the line $X_1 + X_2 = \bar{X}$, shown as $\bar{X}\bar{X}$ in figure 3.6. Because of the convex
nature of the iso-cost curves either $X_1 = \bar{X}$, $X_2 = 0$ or $X_1 = 0$, $X_2 = \bar{X}$ will

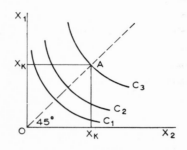

Figure 3.5.

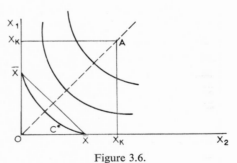

Figure 3.6.

be the division of output on the two machines assuring minimum cost
of C^*. Thus when output is less than machine capacity only one of the
machines will be utilised.

Case (ii) $\qquad\qquad\qquad\qquad X_1 + X_2 = X_K.$

The result is analogous to case (i). Only one machine will be used at full
capacity output.

Case (iii) $\qquad\qquad\qquad\qquad X_K < X_1 + X_2 < 2X_K.$

For any output satisfying this constraint the division of output is given by the line $X_1 + X_2 = \bar{X}$. But the only feasible division of this output, due to the capacity constraints, is along the segment $e_1 e_2$ in figure 3.7. e_1 has co-ordinates $(\bar{X} - X_K, X_K)$ and e_2 has co-ordinates $(X_K, \bar{X} - X_K)$. Thus e_1 and e_2 both lie on the same iso-cost line C^*, which because of the con-

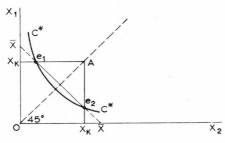

Figure 3.7.

vexity of these iso-cost curves is seen to be the lowest total variable cost for producing $\bar{X}$. Hence when the desired level of output lies between X_K and $2X_K$ one machine will be operated at full capacity and the remaining output will be produced on the other machine.

Case (iv) $$X_1 + X_2 = 2X_K.$$

For this output the only feasible programme is to operate both machines at full capacity.

Using these results for the two-machine plant we may now solve the cost-minimising problem for a plant composed of M machines each of the same size and vintage, and such that the total variable cost function of each machine has the properties specified in (3.24).

For a two-machine plant we have shown that for a level of exogenous demand greater than the size of the machine, total variable cost is minimised by using one machine at full capacity and producing the remaining output on the other machine. This implies that when an exogenous output $\bar{X}$ is to be produced in the M machine plant such that $X_K \leq \bar{X} \leq MX_K$, total variable cost is minimised when as many machines as possible are used at full capacity and the remaining output (if any) is produced on any other machine.

This solution to the problem of optimally using machines in a plant, in the special case of uniformly falling marginal cost for each machine, suggests why it may be implausible to assume that machines operate at the same output at each instant in a thermal electric plant. Load (exogenous output) fluctuates during the hours of a day, so that at certain times it is less than the total capacity of the plant. Thus if the optimisation procedure described here is followed some machines may not be operated at all, and/or one machine may be operated at less than full capacity during these hours.[18] It is more plausible to assume that over the period of a year, for plants composed of machines of the same size and vintage, total output and total fuel input on each machine will be the same. For, if problems of refiring boilers are ignored, and it is assumed that machines may be started and stopped instantaneously, then for less than full operation of plant capacity, it is plausible that the choice of machines to be operated at full capacity, less than full capacity, or not operated, will vary over the year. The reason for this is that depreciation may be assumed to vary as the degree of capacity operation of a machine and the plant operator will be interested in minimising the degree of depreciation on each machine. Thus over the year the output and fuel input on each machine may be taken to be the same.

---

[18] This abstracts from the problem of machines operating hot but not connected to load.

CHAPTER 4

SURVEY AND CRITIQUE OF THE LITERATURE

4.1. Introduction

In this chapter we survey and criticize the empirical studies that have been made of the production operation in the steam-electric power industries of the United States and the United Kingdom. The abundance of published data for plants in this industry (somewhat more abundant for the U.S. than the U.K.) makes it a fruitful field of research for those interested in the electric-power industry as such, and also for economists interested in tests of hypotheses and illustrations of production theory. The following survey is comprehensive and provides sufficient justification for this further study of the production process in steam-electric power.

Any critique of this nature may be based on the "correct" methodology of approaching the problem as viewed by the critic or simply as a criticism of the literature accepting the methodology of the various authors. It is difficult of course to strictly divide a survey into two watertight compartments such as these, thus necessarily this survey will be a combination of both approaches. We shall be more interested in the methods used to estimate production and cost functions for this industry than in a detailed survey of the results obtained by the various authors.

Several general criticisms may be made which apply to a greater or lesser extent to all published studies of the production process in steam-electric power.

(a) The plant or firm has been taken as the unit of observation rather than machines in the plant.
(b) No allowance has been made for the machine-mix of plants.
(c) For some studies no allowance has been made for the effects of technological change or for the mixed vintage of machines in a plant.

(d) The programming technique for minimising variable cost in a plant has not been considered.

(e) The instantaneous nature of the production process in terms of fuel input has generally been ignored and thus the implications of using annual data to estimate instantaneous parameters have not been considered.[1]

(f) Often no allowance has been made for the varied degree of capacity utilisation of machines and where this has been explicitly considered the measures of capacity utilisation used are inappropriate for estimation of the production function.

(g) Two studies assumed cost-minimising behaviour on the part of firms and used the derived behaviour relations as functions to estimate the parameters of the production function. It will be shown that the cost-minimisation behaviour assumed in these studies is not relevant for firms in the electric-power industry. If firms are assumed to follow some cost-minimisation behaviour akin to that implied in micro-economic theory, the form of behaviour relations derived is different from that used in the empirical analyses that have been carried out.

The attempts to estimate parameters of the production function and/or the cost relations may broadly be classified under two headings: those which do not explicitly assume any optimising behaviour on the part of firms in the industry and those studies which explicitly assume optimising behaviour on the part of entrepreneurs.

4.2. Studies which do not explicitly assume optimising behaviour

J. A. NORDIN[2]

Nordin's unit of observation was one steam-electric plant using coal. His interest was solely in explaining fuel costs for this plant and to do this he obtained data for 541 eight-hour shifts in 1941. The relation between fuel costs and output was given by

$$Y = 16.68 + 0.125X + 0.00439X^2 \qquad (4.1)$$

---

[1] See chapter 5 where this problem is shown to be an aggregation problem.
[2] Note on a Light Plant's Cost Curves, *Econometrica*, XV, July 1947, p. 231.

where Y is total fuel cost for an eight-hour period and X is eight-hour total output in per cent of capacity. A third degree equation did not give a significant improvement in fit.

Nordin's study is limited in that it applies to only one plant. However, the plant has only one turbine; thus the machine is easily identified. He seems to be the only author who has realised the instantaneous nature of the production process in terms of fuel input and the fact that the plant can operate at different degrees of capacity in each instant.

"For each eight-hour shift the output was approximated by adding the hourly instantaneous demand readings. Sample checks with a demand meter recording continuously indicated that the approximation was reasonably good. It must be noted that ideally output should be an instantaneous rate; whenever output is represented as a total over a period there is a loss of accuracy."[3]

Presumably he used the same method to derive a measure of fuel input.

K. S. LOMAX[4]

Lomax was interested in obtaining a relation between costs and output. His units of observation were steam-electric plants operating for more than 6600 hours in 1947–48 in two regions of the United Kingdom. For each of these regions a cross-section study was made in the belief that "cross-sectional data...will give a rough approximation to the long-run cost curve, that is, the envelope of the short-run cost curves for individual stations".[5] No allowance is made for the difference in vintage of plants in this sample nor for the varied machine-mix of plants.[6] The steam plants considered use oil, coal and coke, and no allowance is made for the difference in fuel used. But as a very small amount of oil was used in 1947–48 compared with coal this omission would not seriously nullify his analysis. The fact that no allowance is made for differences in technology in plants implies that no separation can be given to the effects of movements along or movements of the production function.

---

[3] *Ibid.*, p. 232.

[4] Cost Curves for Electricity Generation, *Economica*, XIX, May 1952, p. 193.

[5] *Ibid.*, p. 193. See also p. 54 ff. of this chapter.

[6] Nordin includes only stations which have AC generators which excludes the older stations with DC generators. But no allowance is made for differences in vintage of AC generators.

The results he derived are

$$\text{North-East} \quad Y \propto X_1^{-0.12} X_2^{-0.41} \tag{4.2}$$

$$\text{South-East} \quad Y \propto X_1^{-0.15} X_2^{-0.70} \tag{4.3}$$

where Y is costs per unit generated, X_1 is capacity of generators in kilo-watts and X_2 is the load factor. The measure of costs Y relates only to the works cost of generation, i.e., fuel, salaries and wages, maintenance and repairs, and excludes overheads. The paucity of data for most plants made this definition of costs necessary. Some justification for the use of the estimated equations as explaining the movement of total costs was given on the grounds that for a few plants, where full accounts were provided, it seemed that overhead costs moved in the same way as works costs of generation.

The load factor X_2 was defined as

$$X_2 = \text{load factor} = \frac{\text{average instantaneous demand over 8760 hours}}{\text{peak (maximum) demand}}. \tag{4.4}$$

X_2 does not measure the degree of capacity utilisation of a plant but was included in the belief that differences in the load pattern of a plant will produce differences in unit cost – "the lower will be the cost the more uniform is demand".[7]

The results of the regression analysis indicate that for given load patterns unit costs fall as the size of plant increases, and with given size of plant, unit costs fall as the load factor increases. Because of the omission of questions of vintage, machine-mix, and the degree of capacity operation, the interpretation of these results as giving any meaningful measure of returns to scale is limited.

J. JOHNSTON[8]

Johnston estimated long-run and short-run cost functions for a sample of 40 steam-electric plants which existed in the United Kingdom in 1946–47.

---

[7] Lomax, *op. cit.*, p. 195.
[8] *Statistical Cost Analysis*. New York: McGraw-Hill Book Company, 1960, pp. 44–74.

The sample constituted about one-ninth of the number of stations in the industry and about 25 per cent of the important group of stations generating under the direction of the Central Electricity Board, which in total produced about 96.8 per cent of electricity output in 1946–47.

He divided the sample into two groups. The first consisted of plants where the capacity, measured in installed kilowatts, had not altered over the period 1927–28 to 1946–47. There were seventeen plants in this category. For the remaining 23 plants there had been a change in the size of capacity over the period. The first group of plants were used as units of observation to obtain estimates of short-run cost functions and are referred to as "short-period firms", while the second group, the "long-period firms", were used as units of observation in order to obtain estimates of long-run cost relationships.

For each of the short-period firms data were obtained on working costs of generation and output over the period 1927–28 to 1947.[9] The cost estimates correspond roughly to variable costs of economic theory and were deflated to allow for price changes and in the case of fuel cost by an index of the calorific content of coal as well, in order to allow for quality changes in fuel. Capital costs could not be obtained in any adequate form from the data so that the short-period cost functions estimated are total variable cost curves.

For each of the 17 short-period firms a total variable cost curve was fitted of the form

$$Y = a + bX + cX^2 + dT \qquad (4.5)$$

where Y is total deflated working expenses, X is annual output, T is time in years and a, b, c and d are the parameters to be estimated. The introduction of T was meant to explain the combined effects of depreciation, changes in management techniques and production techniques, etc.[10]

The "short-period firms" had constant capacity size but were not of the same vintage. No explicit allowance was made for embodied tech-

[9] Working costs are fuel + salaries and wages + repairs and maintenance.
[10] Johnston, *op. cit.*, p. 54. Johnston used the term obsolescence of plant but presumably he meant depreciation. However obsolescence might also be important if older plants were used at lower capacity levels, e.g. only for peaking purposes. But a full analysis would entail introduction of a capacity factor.

nological change here, the variable T presumably explaining the effect of disembodied technological change as well as depreciation on a plant of fixed size and vintage. No consideration was given to the machine-mix of plants or to the degree of capacity utilisation.[11]

It is possible that while the total capacity size of a plant remained constant the machine-mix in terms of size or vintage altered over the period 1927–28 to 1946–47; but this is unlikely except for plants operating before the beginning of the period, for the life of generators is between 20 and 30 years.[12]

The degree of explanatory power obtained from the fitted equations was high with R^2 being greater than 83 per cent in all cases and having an average value of 94.1 per cent for the best fitting regressions of the 17 short-period firms. Only five of the 17 firms had a regression equation with the coefficient of X^2 significantly different from zero at the 5 per cent level, and for four of these five firms the sign of the coefficient is negative which is contrary to the hypothesis of increasing average variable and marginal cost functions for a quadratic total cost function. Johnston then concludes that

"...the short-period results tend to support the thesis of a linear total cost function with constant AVC and MC curves."[13]

Of the 17 functions 12 have a coefficient of T significantly different from zero at the 5 per cent level. The sign of this coefficient varies among the firms and may be interpreted as deciding for each firm whether the effect of disembodied technological change or depreciation was greater over time.[14]

In order to estimate the long-run cost function Johnston observed only those firms where capacity, measured in installed kilowatts, had changed over the period 1927 to 1948. His reasoning is as follows: if a plant of different capacity size over time is assumed to operate on the long-run

---

[11] Thus the observed output X could in principle be obtained from plants with different machine-mixes and different degrees of capacity utilisation even though the sizes of the plants were identical.

[12] Johnston, *op. cit.*, p. 46

[13] *Ibid.*, p. 57. The addition of total fixed cost to total variable cost simply alters the position of the estimated cost curve.

[14] *Ibid.*, p. 59. The value of T was taken about the central year of observation on each plant as origin.

total cost envelope to the short-run total cost curves, then a regression of cost on output over time will indeed be an estimate of the long-run cost function for the plant.

This implies that, in each year of observation, the firm operates at that output having minimum average cost on the particular short-run total cost function relating to the scale of plant in that year. Also it is implied that there is no technological change so that the long-run total cost function is derived from a fixed production function. Neither of these implications holds for Johnston's long-run analysis so that it is difficult to give meaning to his results other than that they show a regression plane fitted to some time-series data for each plant.

The change in capacity of "long-period firms" generally implies the addition of capacity rather than the construction of a new plant of different scale. The addition of turbines having different production characteristics than existing units compounds the problem of machine-mix in terms of the size of individual units in a plant and their vintage.

The estimation of long-run total costs for each of the 23 plants in the long-period sample is difficult, for data on capital costs were not published. Thus Johnston separated his estimating procedure into two parts. First he estimated the regressions of total working expenses on output and time for each of the 23 long-period firms over the period 1927–28, in exactly the same manner as the short-run total variable cost functions were estimated. As for the short-period functions, the "long-period" total variable cost functions are mainly linear in output X, with or without a significant coefficient for time, T.

The implications of this methodology may be shown graphically. Suppose for a firm we have information on the set of long-run and short-run cost curves, two sets of which are shown in figure 4.1. The set I refers to a plant of smaller capacity than the set II. In the long run if the firm is observed at capacity I then it will be producing at E_I, similarly in the long run it would be producing at E_{II} if observed with capacity II. The appropriate points on the short-run total variable cost curves for each size plant will then be E_I^* and E_{II}^*. Analogous to the long-run total cost curve we then have a long-run total variable cost curve which is the locus of such points E_I^* and E_{II}^*. It is this curve that Johnston is attempting to estimate.

However, if plant size does not change every year, then a plant will be observed at other points than the "optimum" on a particular short-run

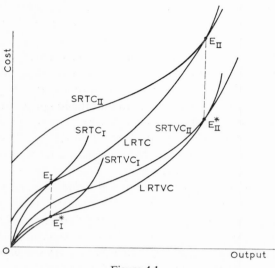

Figure 4.1.

total variable cost curve.[15] If it is assumed that the firm is generally fully adjusted in the long run so that it operates at the point of minimum average cost at each plant scale, the inclusion of the nonoptimal points will produce a regression equation that is not the long-run total variable cost curve.

The fact that there are different vintages of machines in plants prior to and after additions to capacity means that the production function of a firm changes over time. Thus for this additional reason it is difficult to see precisely what Johnston's long-period cost function measures.

He concludes, however, that the long-run relationship of total variable costs to output is linear for a single firm at different levels of plant size.[16] He also carries out two cross-section studies on 40 firms for the year 1946–47 and for 33 firms in 1938–39 and shows a highly significant linear relationship between total working costs and output in both cross sections. These results are said to support the hypothesis that there is a linear relationship between total variable costs and output for firms of varying size.

---

[15] Provided that its output is different.

[16] Johnston, *op. cit.*, p. 66.

Even if it is assumed that the operation of existing plants when observed in the cross sections does take place at the point of minimum average cost on the cost curves relating to he scales of particular plants, the fact that no allowance is made for differing technology in the firms of the cross section means that the estimated regressions cannot be said to be long-run cost functions.[17]

In a cross-section study of 35 of the 40 firms operating in 1946–47, Johnston introduced a proxy for technological change in the form of a measure of the thermal efficiency of plants "to take account of difference in the age, type and efficiency of plants".[18] The fitted regression was of the form

$$Y = AX^\alpha e^{\beta V} \tag{4.6}$$

where Y is total deflated working expenses, X is output and V is thermal efficiency in per cent. This regression performs well, $R^2 = 0.9878$. Johnston holds V constant at its average level for the 35 firms in the sample and thus obtains an alternative estimate of the long-run variable cost curve. If plants are operating at the long-run equilibrium points on their short-run cost curves then this function would show how total working cost varies over plants of different technology and scale. However, it is highly unlikely that all firms in the sample will be in such long-period equilibrium. An additional complication is that thermal efficiency refers to individual machines in the plant, and for the plant as a whole it is not easy to interpret when there is a machine-mix in terms of size and vintage.

The second part of Johnston's long-run analysis is an attempt to estimate long-run capital costs, that is the variation in capital changes as a firm moves from one plant scale to another. There was no available data on capital costs for plants in the British steam-electric power industry so Johnston used data for the United States Industry in an attempt

---

[17] There is an objection that may be made to this criticism. If technological change implies only the introduction of plant of a larger capacity than was previously possible, then in some sense a cross section strictly making no allowance for technological change as such might produce a relevant long-run total variable cost curve. But this assumes that all firms observed are operating at the point of minimum average total cost and abstracts from questions of machine-mix.

[18] Johnston, *op. cit.*, footnote 1, p. 66.

to obtain a relation for long-run capital costs. He uses the results of a survey of American coal plants operating in 1947. Full acknowledgment is given to the shortcomings of the data which reflect capital costs, i.e., land, structures and equipment, valued at historic cost and assessed at 15 per cent per annum.[19] The mixed nature of plants in the sample, in terms of size and vintage of units, obscures any true relationship between fixed charges and installed capacity.[20] He believes, however, that the relatively large number of plants in the sample (73) helps to average out these variations. Johnston computed the regression of Y total fixed costs per annum on X output, and derived

$$Y = 132.3 + 2.6387X \qquad R = 0.9212 . \tag{4.7}$$

The average fixed cost curve derived from this linear total fixed cost equation is approximately linear over most of the output range and seems to describe adequately the variation in the data.

It is difficult to understand why Johnston used a measure of output rather than capacity of plant as the independent variable for estimating capital costs. Unless all plants in the sample operated at the same degree of capacity utilisation or operated at the point of minimum average cost on the short-run total cost function for their particular plant size,[21] capacity of plant would be a better explanatory variable for capital input.

Johnston also introduced the plant factor as a variable in explaining capital input and estimated a function

$$Y = 8.898 \; X^{0.9476} \, e^{-0.11495P} \qquad R^2 = 0.9161 \tag{4.8}$$

---

[19] *Ibid.*, p. 68.

[20] For a consideration of the capital costs in steam-electric power see chapter 6.

[21] If all plants operate at the same degree of capacity utilisation a linear regression of Y on X will have the same Y intercept as a regression of Y on capacity output but will have a slope of $2.6387 \div C$, where $X = CX_K$ and X_K is capacity output. Thus if C were known the "correct" regression could be obtained from (4.7). Similarly if the long-run equilibrium point on each short-run total cost curve were at the same per cent of capacity, and firms actually operated here, the "correct" regression could be obtained in the same way. Explicit consideration of machine-mix renders the task of explaining fixed costs more difficult.

where Y and X are defined as above and P is the plant factor.[22] Since capital costs are independent of the level of plant operation, being essentially fixed costs, it is difficult to give meaning to the introduction of the plant factor as an explanatory variable of fixed cost.

In his long-run analysis both the fixed and variable components of the "long-run total cost curve" were found to be linear. Thus the long-run average cost in Johnston's analysis has the same basic shape as its components, falling steeply at first and then becoming approximately constant over the greater part of the output range.[23] Support is given to this contention that long-run average costs are constant by the estimation of equation (4.9) which explicitly introduces the size of plant Z, measured in kilowatts of installed capacity, for a cross section of 56 plants operating in 1946–47

$$Y = a + b_1 X + b_2 X^2 + cXZ + d_1 Z + d_2 Z^2. \qquad (4.9)$$

When plant size, Z, is considered a parameter, the computed average variable cost curves for varying Z yield a set of average variable cost curves having their minima almost on a horizontal straight line.

We see then that there are many criticisms that may be made of Johnston's analysis on the basis of his own methodology and view of the production process in the industry. It must be agreed with Johnston that his short-run analysis is of more value than his long-run analysis. The conclusion that average total cost is constant in the long run is compatible with a linear homogeneous production function for steam-electric power, but the shortcomings of the analysis prevent any valid conclusions regarding either the cost structure of the industry in the long run compatible with *a priori* cost curves of micro-economic analysis, or of the nature of the production function.

R. KOMIYA[24]

Komiya is interested in explaining shifts in the production process due

---

[22] For a definition of the plant factor see chapter 3.

[23] Johnston, *op. cit.*, p. 72.

[24] Technological Progress and the Production Function in the United States Steam Power Industry, *The Review of Economics and Statistics*, XLIV, May 1962, p. 156.

to technological change in the steam-electric power industry. To do this he observes only new plants built over the period 1930 to 1956 and classifies them in terms of the year they were built and the nature of the fuel used. A plant built in a particular year is assumed to embody the technology available at that time, hence if differences in the production function are observed between these vintage groups this would be evidence of shifts of the production function due to technological change. The plants are also classified into coal and non-coal plants where a non-coal plant is defined as a plant which is not equipped with coal-burning equipment. The rationale for this is that differences in the production process may not only be due to technological change but will also depend on whether a plant is equipped to burn coal or not. The 235 plants in his sample were divided into four vintage groups,[25] and each vintage group into a coal and non-coal group. For each of these eight cells a production function was calculated and the analysis of covariance was used to test whether the estimated functions differed significantly between cells.

Essentially Komiya was interested in ex-ante relationships between inputs and outputs. His data were adjusted to full capacity working of plants so that the results he obtained can only be interpreted as applying to the operation of plants at full capacity. No investigation was made of the nature of ex-post production relations allowing for varied degrees of capacity utilisation. But in adjusting to full capacity operation a significant error may have been made as we shall see. The variables that Komiya used were,

X_1 = the average size of generating unit in megawatts;

Y_f = fuel input per generating unit when operating at capacity level of operation in terms of BTU's per hour;

Y_c = capital cost of equipment in constant (1947) dollars per generating unit. The costs of construction and land were excluded;

Y_l = the average number of employees during the year per generating unit;

X_2 = the number of generating units on the same plant.

Each plant entered the sample only once, when new, and never appears again in the sample.[26] The published fuel input could be deflated by the

---

[25] 1930–45, 1946–50, 1951–53, 1954–56.

[26] Presumably in the first year after the plant was built.

published plant factor (PF) to obtain a measure of fuel input per hour at capacity. However, this procedure leads to an incorrect measure of capacity fuel input. This implied process of deflation, used to obtain a capacity estimate of fuel input, is shown in figure 4.2a. Let a be input of fuel (in

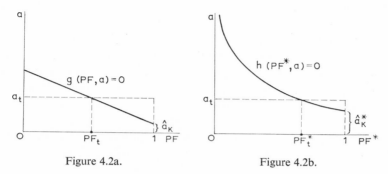

Figure 4.2a.   Figure 4.2b.

BTU's) per hour of generation and suppose that a_t and PF_t are the observations on a plant.[27] Then $\hat{a}_K$, an estimate of capacity fuel input is obtained from

$$\hat{a}_K = PF_t a_t. \qquad (4.10)$$

This implies a relation

$$g(PF, a) = a + a_t PF - a_t(1 + PF_t) = 0 \qquad (4.11)$$

which is linear in a and PF.

This procedure is incorrect for as has been shown in chapter 3 (pp. 42–45) the correct measure of the level of capacity operation is not PF but PF*. In general PF underestimates the degree of capacity utilisation.[28] Thus the plant will actually be observed at (PF_t^*, a_t) in figure 4.2b where the relation between fuel input and the level of capacity operation is given by the function h which is unknown.[29] Further, the position and shape of

---

[27] For the purposes of this argument the plant is assumed to consist of only one machine. If the plant consists of more than one machine further complications are added to the analysis.

[28] See chapter 3, p. 40.

[29] See chapter 5 for estimates of the h function. The h function is simply the ex-post production function if problems concerned with the period of production are ignored.

the h function will in general depend on the size and vintage of units in the plant. This error would not be serious if plants operated at a PF of approximately 100 per cent in their first year of full operation, but an examination of the data shows this not in general to have been the case. Thus we conclude that such estimates of the fuel input at full capacity levels of operation are in principle in error.[30]

Labour input was not deflated to the level of full capacity utilisation of plants, but this does not seriously jeopardise his results, for labour input is relatively unaffected by the degree of capacity utilisation over a significantly wide range.[31] Similarly the only deflation process involved with capital was in terms of the price of capital, since capital cost does not vary with the degree of capacity utilisation.

Two forms of the production function were fitted by Komiya for each of the eight vintage fuel-type cells. First he tried a Cobb–Douglas of the form

$$X_1 = KY_f^{\delta_1} Y_c^{\delta_2} Y_l^{\delta_3} X_2^{\delta_4} \qquad (4.12)$$

which was unsuccessful. He then fitted a limitational model akin to a Leontief-type fixed proportion production function where the input coefficients vary according to scale and vintage.

$$Y_f = A_f X_1^{\beta_F}, \qquad (4.13)$$

$$Y_c = A_c X_1^{\beta_c} X_2^{\mu_c}, \qquad (4.14)$$

$$Y_l = A_l X_1^{\beta_l} X_2^{\mu_l}. \qquad (4.15)$$

There is a problem here concerning machine-mix of plants. The unit of observation was the plant rather than the turbine-generator unit. Thus if some plants in the sample were composed of units of different sizes the

---

[30] I am not certain that Komiya used this procedure to estimate fuel input at capacity. In private correspondence he suggested that at high levels of capacity operation, near 100 per cent, fuel input is proportional to output. Thus his estimated a_t would be constant over a significantly wide range of utilisation (but see chapter 5). Also plants in their first year of operation do not in general operate at near 100 per cent of capacity.
[31] See chapter 6 for a discussion of labour input.

interpretation of this limitational model would be difficult, for the independent variable X_1 and the dependent variables would be averages which could not plausibly be used in a production process essentially based on machines rather than plants. For example, suppose we have two plants each with two units. However, in one plant the units are 50 MW and 150 MW while in the second plant the units are 10 MW and 190 MW. The use of this limitational model would imply that fuel, capital and labour requirements would be the same for the two plants. Thus if plants were included in the sample which were composed of units of different sizes the meaning of the ex-ante production function in terms of Komiya's limitational model is obscured.[32] If, however, the sample of plants included only those plants having the same sizes of units then the model could reasonably be used as a production model and the inclusion of X_2, the number of units, in (4.14) and (4.15) would measure economies in capital and labour input when the number of units in a plant of equal sized units is increased.[33]

Komiya considers the problem of whether the units of observation should be machines or plants. He states that a capital equation on a unit basis might be expressed as

$$Y_c = A'_c X_1^{\beta_c'} \qquad (4.16)$$

while one on a plant basis might be expressed as

$$Y_c X_2 = A''_c (X_1 X_2)^{\beta_c''} \qquad (4.17)$$

or

$$Y_c = A_c X_1^{\beta_c''} X_1^{(\beta_c'' - 1)}. \qquad (4.18)$$

Clearly equations (4.16) and (4.18) are special cases of (4.14). The question arises whether (4.16) or (4.14) should be used as the estimating equation for capital input. Komiya estimated (4.14) and tested to see whether the estimate m_c of μ_c was significantly different from zero or $b_c - 1$ where b_c is the estimate of β_c. If m_c is significantly different from zero and

---

[32] In private communication with Professor Komiya he suggested that not very many plants in his sample were composed of units of different size.
[33] See chapter 5.

$b_c - 1$ then (4.14) shows that the scale effect on capital input operates both on a unit basis and a plant basis – that is, it depends on the number of units in the plant as well as their average size. If this is not the case, then the input of capital per unit depends only on the average size of units and equation (4.16) may be used.

However, equation (4.17) implies that for a plant of a given capacity, $X_1 X_2$, the capital cost of equipment, $Y_c X_2$, is independent of the machine-mix in the plant, thus (4.18) is not a reasonable expression for capital input per machine, and the test used by Komiya to determine whether (4.14) or (4.16) should be the expression for capital input has little relevance. Equation (4.14) as it stands is a reasonable expression for capital input if problems of machine-mix are ignored.

The same procedure was applied to the labour equation (4.15). In this case the criticism of the procedure may not be quite as strong, for it is more reasonable to assume that total labour input depends only on total capacity of the plant and varies far less than capital input with variations in machine-mix of plants. But even in this case it is likely that variations in machine-mix for plants of a given total size do entail differences in labour input.

Fitting the fuel equation (4.13) to the eight vintage fuel-type cells Komiya found that the analysis of covariance supports a model with a constant parameter $\hat{\beta}_f$ but with differences in the constant term $\hat{A}_f$. Thus the effect of technological change as it applies to fuel input is to shift the function but to leave the scale effects constant over time both for coal and non-coal plants. The value of $\hat{\beta}_f$ is significantly smaller than unity which indicates that economies of scale are important, i.e. as the average size of unit in the plant increases the input of fuel at capacity operation falls for any vintage fuel-type classification. The shifts in the function were not uniform and were not significant among the vintage periods 1946–50, 1951–53 and 1954–56. However, the signs of the differences between the constant terms in the regressions are positive, which indicate that the effect of technological change has been to reduce fuel requirements. There appears to be some difference between coal and non-coal plants and Komiya concluded that a coal plant requires from 2 to 3 per cent less fuel than a non-coal plant of the same scale.

Considering capital input, Komiya found that the most appropriate model suggested was one which implied constant scale parameters for all vintage fuel-type cells and a difference in the constant term due only to differences in fuel input but constant over time. All shifts in the constant term that related to technological change turned out to be non-significant.

$\hat{\mu}_c$ was found to be significantly different from $\hat{\beta}_c - 1$, so equation (4.14) was accepted as a reasonable interpretation of capital input, implying that both the average size of generating units and the number of units exercise an effect on the equipment cost per generating unit. $\hat{\beta}_c$ and $\hat{\mu}_c$ are both smaller than unity, implying that equipment cost per generator falls as the number of units in a plant increases but the average size of units remains the same, or is smaller for a plant having the same number of units as another, but different average size of units.

Differences between the capital requirements of coal and non-coal plants was substantial, implying that a coal plant requires up to 25 per cent more capital than a non-coal plant of the same size.

The fitted labour-input functions (4.15) were less satisfactory than the capital- or fuel-input functions, explaining about 79 per cent of the variation in labour input compared with more than 95 per cent in the case of capital and fuel.[34] Estimates of the constant term and of the scale parameters vary randomly between the vintage fuel-type cells, and no overall regression model was accepted on the basis of the analysis of covariance performed. The sum of the absolute values of $\hat{\beta}_l$ and $\hat{\mu}_l$ generally does not differ significantly from zero, implying from equations (4.17) and (4.18) that the plant size, $X_1 X_2$, rather than the size and number of generating units, is the relevant variable in determining labour input. The values of $\hat{\beta}_l$ and $\hat{\mu}_l$ varied widely, however $\hat{\beta}_l$ was greater than unity in all the cells while $\hat{\mu}_l$ was less than unity in each cell, thus the implications for returns to scale in terms of labour requirements are mixed. The differences between the scale parameters for coal and non-coal plants were not significant except for the 1951–53 vintage group, but differences between the constant terms for coal and non-coal plants suggest that the labour requirements are lower for non-coal plants. No conclusion could be drawn regarding the effect of technological change because of the difficulty of accepting one regression model that would adequately explain the data over the eight vintage fuel-type cells. A model was assumed which implied separate regression lines for non-coal and coal plants, with common scale

---

[34] This was the highest R^2 for the labour-input function for the vintage fuel-type cells.

parameters for each regression in the fuel type but allowing the effect of technological change to be expressed in different constant terms for each of the vintage fuel-type cells. For this model the effect of technological change was to reduce labour input for a coal plant of a given size by 46 per cent from vintage 1930–45 to vintage 1954–56. For non-coal plants the reduction over this period was 18 per cent.

The stratification technique used by Komiya is interesting and is employed in this study.[35] However, his limitational model is defective especially as regards fuel input. The labour- and capital-input functions he used abstract from the problem of machine-mix and his results for labour input are not too satisfactory. But in general the methodological approach of Komiya is sound and provides a basis for distinguishing between shifts along and shifts of the production function that are meaningful; in that, the effects of technological change and changes in scale may be separated if only at the level of full capacity operation of equipment.

Y. BARZEL[36]

In order to explain the production process in steam-electric power generation Barzel estimated input functions for fuel, labour and capital without explicitly assuming any cost-minimising behaviour on the part of entrepreneurs. His unit of observation was the plant and his sample consisted of 220 plants installed between 1941 and 1959 in the United States.[37] Each plant was observed from its first full year of operation, annually, until any major change took place in it or until 1960. Thus there is no consideration of machine-mix of plants in this study.

The input function for fuel and labour is estimated in log linear form

$$\log y = \sum_i b_i \log x_i \qquad i = 0, ..., 19. \tag{4.19}$$

The dependent variable is total input of fuel or the average number of employees in the year of observation. The set of dependent variables, x_i, are the same for the fuel and labour equation:

x_0 is a constant;

---

[35] See chapter 5.

[36] The Production Function and Technical Change in the Steam-Power Industry, *The Journal of Political Economy*, LXXII, April 1964, p. 133.

[37] For the capital-input function only 178 plants provided adequate data.

x_1 is plant size measured by the number of kilowatts of installed capacity;

x_2 is said to be the anticipated average load of plant measured by the observed load factor in the first full year of operation;

x_3 is a within-plant index of x_2 over time;

x_4 is the anticipated average input price ratio measured as the ratio of the average price of fuel per BTU to the average labour cost per man-year in the first year of operation of the plant;

x_5 is a within-plant index of x_4 over time;

x_6 is the age of plant defined as the accumulated number of hours of operation;

$x_7 - x_{19}$ define a set of dummy variables where x_7 has a value of 10 for plants that started operation in 1943 and 1 for other years. $x_8 - x_{19}$ are similarly defined for 1948–59 plants. (The log transformation converts the dummies to 1 and 0.)

The "load factor" x_2 used by Barzel in fact seems to be the published plant factor.[38] He erroneously defines it as the percentage of the annual number of hours in which a plant is utilised. This will not be the case unless in each hour when the plant operates hot and connected to load it does so at full capacity.[39] The rationale for x_2 is that Barzel introduces another dimension (besides size and vintage) to the nature of capital in a plant. He considers that two plants of the same capacity (total installed kilowatts) and vintage may be designed to operate most effectively at different levels of capacity utilisation. Thus the designed degree of capacity utilisation affects fuel and labour requirements. Barzel uses as a proxy for this designed degree of capacity utilisation the observed plant factor in the first full year of operation. But, as we have seen, the plant factor is not the relevant measure of capacity operation for the production function.

The use of the intra-plant load index x_3 defined as PF_t/x_2, where PF_t is the plant factor in the year of observation, is intended to measure fluctuations in fuel and labour input when the plant operates at other than the designed level of capacity x_2.

---

[38] Barzel, *op. cit.*, footnote 3, p. 134. The term "load factor" as used has another meaning. See p. 54 above.

[39] See chapter 3.

The introduction of variables x_4 and x_5 is explained similarly to x_2 and x_3, but an important point is introduced here. Barzel assumes that there is ex-ante substitution between capital, fuel and labour, in that the nature of equipment installed depends on factor price ratios. Thus anticipated price ratios will affect the type of installed equipment. Barzel uses only first-year price ratios as proxies for these anticipated price ratios but does not consider the price of capital (which is understandable due to difficulties of defining and measuring the variable). The nature of technological change, measured by the dummy variables which shift the constant term, takes on a special meaning and is actual rather than virtual technological change. It is possible that factor price ratios may be such that the latest technology cannot profitably be installed. Alternatively technological change may progress in such a way that whatever actual price ratios are, the installation of a plant at time t embodies more "technology" than one of the same size installed in $t-1$, even though prices were unchanged in the two periods.

It is difficult to see what meaning can be given to x_5 in the fuel- and labour-input functions. x_5 is defined as x_{4t}/x_4 where x_{4t} is the factor price ratio for the plant at time t. If fuel or labour input were affected by changes in the factor price ratio over time, this would imply that there is ex-post substitution between labour and fuel in electric-power generation which is distinctly implausible.

The estimated fuel equation was

$$y = 0.896x_1 + 0.848x_2 + 0.893x_3 - 0.040x_4 - 0.074x_5 - 0.013x_6$$
$$+ [\text{constant} + \text{dummy variables}] \qquad R^2 = 0.9904. \qquad (4.20)$$

Economies of scale are important in this formulation ($\hat{b}_1$ is significantly different from unity). The variables x_1, x_2 and x_3 explain the bulk of the variation in fuel input, both intra- and inter-plant, the remaining coefficients are only of minor importance. Both $\hat{b}_4$ and $\hat{b}_5$ are significantly different from zero implying that the greater is the anticipated fuel labour price ratio the less fuel-intensive will be initial investment in plant. But little meaning can be given to $\hat{b}_5$. $\hat{b}_6$ was not significantly different from zero and when an alternative definition of age – years of existence of plant – was used, the results did not change significantly. Thus depreciation of the plant in terms of the efficiency of fuel use seems to be negligible.

In order to detect the effect of technological change Barzel first estimated a separate regression for plants of each vintage year. It appeared that the only difference between these regressions was in the constant term, thus there would seem to be justification in estimating the effects of technological change by the inclusion of dummy variables in (4.19). The pattern of shifts in the function represented by variation in the coefficients of the dummy variables is not uniform and not all the $\hat{b}_i$, $i = 7, ..., 19$, are significantly different from zero. The effect of technological change is quite small with a 9.6 per cent reduction in fuel requirements for one kilowatthour of electricity between 1941 and 1959.

The estimated labour-input function was

$$y = 0.626x_1 + 0.169x_2 + 0.054x_3 - 0.267x_4 - 0.259x_5 + 0.010x_6$$

$$+ [\text{constant} + \text{dummy variables}] \qquad R^2 = 0.8079. \qquad (4.21)$$

The poorer degree of explanatory power in the labour-input equation when compared with the fuel equation is partly explained by the measure of labour input used (average number of employees).[40] There was also less justification for including all the plants in a single regression equation for labour input, for when individual regressions were estimated for each vintage year the regression coefficients as well as the constant terms were not stable from year to year.

The degree of returns to scale is greater for labour input than fuel input. $\hat{b}_1$ is relatively stable in the individual year regressions and the pooled regression. $\hat{b}_2$, the coefficient of the "load factor", is significantly different from zero but small, so that differences in the anticipated level of capacity operation for plants of the same size does not significantly affect the required labour input. $\hat{b}_3$ is not significantly different from zero, implying that variations in capacity utilisation do not affect labour input. The coefficients of x_4 and x_5 are both negative and significantly different from zero, implying that an increase in the anticipated fuel labour price ratio leads to a reduction in labour input. The effect of depreciation based on accumulated use was not significant but when a variable measuring calen-

---

[40] An attempt to improve this variable by using total number of hours worked per year did not improve the results.

dar years of operation was also introduced, both variables significantly affected fuel input, the accumulated use of plant had a positive coefficient while the years of plant operation had a negative coefficient. Barzel explains this in terms of increased maintenance, reflected in the accumulated use variable, and a combination of increased quality of labour and disembodied technological change affecting the labour input reflected in the negative coefficient of accumulated years of operation.

The coefficients of the dummy variables are not all significant but show a shift in the function due to technological change which resulted in labour requirements being lower in 1959 than in 1941. The effect of technological change on saving labour input appears to be stronger than for fuel input.

To explain capital input Barzel estimated a function (4.22) for 178 plants in the sample:

$$K = 0.815 \,(\text{size}) + 0.271 \,(\text{labour price}) + 0.186 \,(\text{fuel price})$$

$$+ \,0.116 \,(\text{load factor}) + \text{dummies.} \qquad R^2 = 0.9437. \qquad (4.22)$$

K is total undeflated value of the plant including equipment, structures and land.[41] Size is x_1 as defined above. The labour price and fuel price variables were those observed in the first full year of operation of the plant and are proxies for anticipated prices. The rationale for their inclusion is to explain the effect of ex-ante substitution between factors which affect the nature of investment. The load factor variable is x_2 as defined above and is included by Barzel in the belief that the anticipated level of capacity operation will affect the quantity of investment in a plant. Presumably the greater is the anticipated degree of capacity operation for plants of a given size and vintage the higher will be the cost of equipment.

It is implicitly assumed that the price of capital is the same for all plants in any year, thus the prices of fuel and labour are basically price ratios. But the prices of capital, fuel and labour are not constant over time

---

[41] A separate regression for equipment only was calculated; the size coefficient was approximately the same; the others were 0.223, 0.127, 0.088 for labour price, fuel price and the load factor respectively.

so that the dummy variables explaining a shift in the capital-input function are compounded of the effects of price changes and of changes in technology. Barzell attempted to separate these two components of the trend term by estimating a function

$$\begin{matrix} \text{coefficients of dummy} \\ \text{variables in} \\ \text{capital equation} \end{matrix} = f \begin{bmatrix} \text{some measure of price change of} \\ \text{capital; dummy variables from} \\ \text{price and labour regressions} \end{bmatrix}$$

The dummy variables from the fuel and labour regressions were used to explain changes in quality of equipment. The results of this procedure were not too satisfactory. Thus Barzel's analysis of capital input does not adequately show the effects of technological change.

Barzel's study is interesting in his method of measuring technological change and his incorporation of factor price ratios to determine the degree of ex-ante substitution between factors, which is reflected in the type of equipment and plant installed. He omits a discussion of machine-mix and the measure of capacity utilisation he uses is not correct.

W. IULO[42]

Finally, mention should be made of this study by Iulo, which for a sample of electric utilities estimates a function relating unit cost of electricity to a set of "historical", "operating" and "market" characteristics. The unit of observation was the firm and the sample included firms which bought electricity from other producers and which generated electricity in hydro-electric works. This study makes no attempt to estimate a production function but simply sets out to explain unit cost without any implicit or explicit assumption concerning the nature of the production process.

We have now discussed the empirical studies of the steam-electric power industry which did not explicitly assume any optimising behaviour on the part of entrepreneurs in this industry. What follows is a critique of two studies which assumed that entrepreneurs follow the traditional cost-minimising behaviour of micro-economic theory.

---

[42] *Electric Utilities – Costs and Performance*, Washington State University Press, 1961.

4.3.   Studies which explicitly assume optimising behaviour

M. NERLOVE[43]

Nerlove attempts to measure the degree of returns to scale in the production of electric power in steam-electric plants in the United States. He considers a cross section of 145 firms operating in 44 states in 1955. The unit of observation is the firm which in general consists of a number of plants. The rationale for concentration on the firm is that primary concern with "the general question of public regulation and investment decisions and the like" would suggest that "the economically relevant entity if the firm. Firms, not plants are regulated, and it is at the level of the firm that investment decisions are made."[44] Thus in this study there is no consideration of machine-mix in terms of the size of units in a plant, nor of plant-mix in terms of the number and sizes of plants in a firm. Nerlove also abstracts from all questions of technological change so that no consideration is given to the different vintages of machines, plants or firms. Thus his results are compounded of movements along and movements of the production function and no meaningful measure of returns to scale in terms of movement along a temporally unchanged production function is possible.

The method followed by Nerlove is to use the long-run total cost function as a reduced form equation to estimate the parameters of a production function. He assumes that the production process of firms in the industry is Cobb–Douglas and the same for all firms

$$y = a_0 x_1^{a_1} x_2^{a_2} x_3^{a_3} u \qquad (4.23)$$

where y, x_1, x_2, x_3 are respectively output in kilowatt hours of generation, labour, capital and fuel input. The a_i are parameters to be estimated and u is a residual or error term which is said to express neutral variations among firms.

Minimisation of total costs (4.24) subject to the constraint

$$c = p_1 x_1 + p_2 x_2 + p_3 x_3 \qquad (4.24)$$

---

[43] Returns to Scale in Electricity Supply, *Measurement in Economics: Studies in Mathematical Economics and Econometrics in Memory of Yehuda Grunfeld.* Stanford: Stanford University Press, 1963, pp. 167–198.
[44] *Ibid.,* p. 167.

imposed by (4.23) yields the familiar long-run total cost function

$$c = ky^{1/r}p_1^{a_1/r}p_2^{a_2/r}p_3^{a_3/r}v,\qquad(4.25)$$

where

$$k = r\left(a_0 a_1^{a_1}a_2^{a_2}a_3^{a_3}\right)^{-1/r},$$
$$v = u^{-1/r},$$
$$r = a_1 + a_2 + a_3.$$

The cost function (4.25) may then be estimated in log linear form (4.26), where capital letters stand for the logarithms of the lower case variables

$$C = K + \frac{1}{r}Y + \frac{a_1}{r}P_1 + \frac{a_2}{r}P_2 + \frac{a_3}{r}P_3 + V.\qquad(4.26)$$

It is necessary to impose the restriction that the coefficients of the prices sum to unity. Nerlove does this by dividing total costs and two of the prices by the remaining price, say the fuel price, to derive his model A,

$$C - P_3 = K + \frac{1}{r}Y + \frac{a_1}{r}(P_1 - P_3) + \frac{a_2}{r}(P_2 - P_3) + V.\qquad(4.27)$$

The measurement of the capital component of costs and of capital "price" poses the greatest difficulties. Nerlove abstracts from the difficulty of measuring the price of capital by assuming that it is the same for all firms. This assumption then implies his model B,

$$C = K' + \frac{1}{r}Y + \frac{a_1}{r}P_1 + \frac{a_3}{r}P_3 + V\qquad(4.28)$$

where $K' = K + (a_2/r)P_2$.

   If either model A or model B is estimated then the degree of returns to scale is given by the reciprocal of the coefficient of output Y, and estimates of the individual parameters of the production function (4.23) may be obtained.

   This procedure implies that in the year of observation each firm in the industry is in long-period equilibrium, in that it is able to adjust the level of all its inputs in order to minimise total costs of the observed output Y, which is considered to be exogenous. Factor prices vary between firms. Thus each firm is assumed to be at a particular point on its long-run expansion path and long-run cost curve. These cost curves will vary between firms even though the underlying technology is assumed to be the same for each firm, because factor prices differ over the cross section. The estimation of model A or B simply fits a production function which implies a firm in such a long-period equilibrium, given its observed level of total costs, output and factor prices.

This analysis, however, is not appropriate for any industry where capital input cannot be readily altered in each period to meet a fluctuating and exogenous output.[45] This is especially true in the steam-electric power industry where plants once installed have a working life of between twenty and thirty years. The cost-minimisation procedure employed by Nerlove does not take into account the nature of capital as truly fixed for firms in the industry. Thus the one-period cost-minimisation procedure is an incorrect description of the behaviour of firms if they are assumed to minimise total cost by some process akin to that implied by traditional micro-economic analysis. Nerlove's approach will be shown to result in an incorrect formulation of the cost structure. The cost function which he uses to estimate the parameters of the production function is not the function that would imply cost minimisation by firms in the steam-electric power industry; it is simply not relevant to the firm operating in this industry as a cost minimiser. Thus the parameters derived and the measure of returns to scale cannot be conceptually correct.

To simplify the analysis consider any industry where the production process is specified at the firm level by a Cobb–Douglas production func-

---

[45] Nerlove, *op. cit.*, p. 168, mentions an objection to the cost-minimisation analysis he uses on the basis that it is implicitly static, but does not point out the implications for his cost-minimisation procedure. C.f. (a) H. B. CHENERY, Overcapacity and the Acceleration Principle, *Econometrica* XX, January 1952, p. 1, who discusses the investment programme over time in terms of minimising discounted net cost with respect to scale of plant; (b) Y. MUNDLAK, Estimation of Production and Behavioral Functions from a Combination of Cross-Section and Time-Series Data, *Measurement in Economics: Studies in Mathematical Economics and Econometrics in Memory of Yehuda Grunfeld*, Stanford: Stanford University Press, 1963, pp. 138–166, who discusses the estimation of production functions from reduced form equations when some of the factors are fixed.

tion (4.29), where output Q is produced by inputs of capital K and labor L. Inputs and outputs refer to a unit time period.

$$Q = AK^{\alpha}L^{\beta}. \tag{4.29}$$

The industry is characterised by two factors: (i) output is known and exogenously determined and (ii) capital is a fixed factor with a life of many unit time periods. If characteristic (ii) is ignored and it is assumed that in any one period the firm minimises total costs of producing Q, the derived long-run cost function is

$$C_{\mathrm{LR}} = \left(\frac{Q}{A}\right)^{\frac{1}{\alpha+\beta}}(\alpha + \beta)\left(\frac{P_K}{\alpha}\right)^{\frac{\alpha}{\alpha+\beta}}\left(\frac{P_L}{\beta}\right)^{\frac{\beta}{\alpha+\beta}} \tag{4.30}$$

where P_K and P_L are the unit prices of capital and labour. The inputs of capital and labour used to produce Q are

$$K = \left[\frac{P_L}{P_K}\frac{\alpha}{\beta}\right]^{\frac{\beta}{\alpha+\beta}}\left(\frac{Q}{A}\right)^{\frac{1}{\alpha+\beta}}, \tag{4.31}$$

and

$$L = \left[\frac{P_K}{P_L}\frac{\beta}{\alpha}\right]^{\frac{\alpha}{\alpha+\beta}}\left(\frac{Q}{A}\right)^{\frac{1}{\alpha+\beta}}. \tag{4.32}$$

The short-run cost function for the firm operating at this level of capacity is

$$C_{\mathrm{SR}} = P_K K + P_L\left[\frac{Q}{AK^{\alpha}}\right]^{\frac{1}{\beta}} \tag{4.33}$$

where K is given by (4.31).

This is the standard cost-minimisation procedure and the estimation of (4.30) implies that each firm is at a point like E_1 in figure 4.3 (the curves and those which follow are schematic and are not exact representations of the cost curves derived from the Cobb–Douglas function).

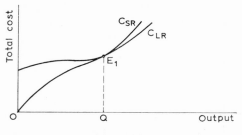

Figure 4.3.

The second characteristic of the industry must now be introduced. Suppose that capital once installed has a life of T unit periods.[46] The firm, then, must carry out a cost-minimisation procedure in T-period terms rather than in one-period terms. Output is exogenously determined and it may be supposed that the firm knows its outputs Q_i over the T periods, or alternatively, it makes forecasts of these outputs on which the investment decision is based. Further, it will be assumed that all the necessary investment for meeting demand over the T periods must be carried out prior to the beginning of the T-period planning horizon, so that no time path of investments is considered.[47] The correct cost-minimisation procedure would then be as follows:

To minimise

$$C = P_L \sum_{i=1}^{T} L_i + T P_K K$$

subject to

$$Q_i = F(K, L_i) \qquad i = 1, ..., T \qquad (4.34)$$

where L_i is labour input in period i and P_L, P_K are the unit prices of labour and capital which are assumed to be constant over time. To simplify

---

[46] Problems of obsolescence and depreciation are not considered here. Their introduction would modify the analysis.

[47] In the steam-electric power industry for a plant this is likely to be the case, with additions to total capacity being made by additional plants, rather than by adding to existing plants after an initial period of installation. However, additions to plant are by no means unknown so that the investment decision in terms of a time pattern of investment should really be considered. But to simplify the analysis it will not be included here.

matters no discount factors are introduced. This procedure yields the lagrangian (4.35), where the λ_i are T lagrangian multipliers.

$$Z = P_L \sum_{i=1}^{T} L_i + TP_K K + \sum_{i=1}^{T} \lambda_i [Q_i - F(K, L_i)]. \qquad (4.35)$$

Then the first order conditions for cost minimisation are

$$\frac{\partial Z}{\partial K} = TP_K - \sum_{i=1}^{T} \lambda_i \frac{\partial F}{\partial K} = 0 \qquad (4.36)$$

$$\frac{\partial Z}{\partial L_i} = P_L - \lambda_i \left| \frac{\partial F}{\partial L} \right|_{L=L_i} = 0 \qquad i = 1, ..., T, \qquad (4.37)$$

$$\frac{\partial Z}{\partial \lambda_i} = Q_i - F[K, L_i] = 0 \qquad i = 1, ..., T. \qquad (4.38)$$

From (4.37)

$$\lambda_i = P_L \left[\frac{\partial F}{\partial L} \Big|_{L=L_i} \right]^{-1} \qquad (4.39)$$

and substituting for (4.39) in (4.36) gives

$$TP_K - P_L \sum_{i=1}^{T} \frac{\partial F}{\partial K} \Big/ \frac{\partial F}{\partial L} \Big|_{L=L_i} = 0. \qquad (4.40)$$

Now for the Cobb–Douglas (4.29)

$$\frac{\partial F}{\partial K} \Big/ \frac{\partial F}{\partial L} = \frac{\alpha}{\beta} \frac{L}{K}. \qquad (4.41)$$

Thus substituting (4.41) in (4.40) we derive

$$TP_K - \frac{\alpha}{\beta} \frac{P_L}{K} \sum_{i=1}^{T} L_i = 0. \qquad (4.42)$$

From (4.29)

$$L_i = \left(\frac{Q_i}{A}\right)^{\frac{1}{\beta}} K^{-\frac{\alpha}{\beta}} \tag{4.43}$$

and substituting for L_i in (4.42)

$$TP_K - \frac{\alpha}{\beta}\frac{P_L}{K}\left[\frac{K^{-\alpha}}{A}\right]^{\frac{1}{\beta}} \sum_{i=1}^{T} Q_i^{\frac{1}{\beta}} = 0. \tag{4.44}$$

Solving for K we have

$$K = \left[\left(\frac{1}{T}\sum_{i=1}^{T} Q_i^{\frac{1}{\beta}}\right) A^{-\frac{1}{\beta}} \frac{\alpha P_L}{\beta P_K}\right]^{\frac{\beta}{\alpha+\beta}} \tag{4.45}$$

and substituting for K in (4.43)

$$L_i = \left(\frac{Q_i}{A}\right)^{\frac{1}{\beta}} \left[\left(\frac{1}{T}\sum_{i=1}^{T} Q_i^{\frac{1}{\beta}}\right) A^{-\frac{1}{\beta}} \frac{\alpha P_L}{\beta P_K}\right]^{-\frac{\alpha}{\alpha+\beta}}. \tag{4.46}$$

Thus the cost-minimisation procedure determines the input of capital K given by (4.45) which is fixed for each of the T unit periods and which is a function of factor prices and the exogenous demands Q_i. The labour input in any unit period (4.46) depends on the output of that period, factor prices and the demands over the complete planning period.

The total cost function for producing the output vector $(Q_1, Q_2, ..., Q_T)$ at minimum cost may be derived and is given by

$$C^T = T^{\frac{\alpha}{\alpha+\beta}}(\alpha + \beta) A^{-\frac{1}{\alpha+\beta}} \left(\frac{P_L}{\beta}\right)^{\frac{\beta}{\alpha+\beta}} \left(\frac{P_K}{\alpha}\right)^{\frac{\alpha}{\alpha+\beta}} \left[\sum_{i=1}^{T} Q_i^{\frac{1}{\beta}}\right]^{\frac{\beta}{\alpha+\beta}}. \tag{4.47}$$

When Q_i is constant for all i we have that

$$C^T = TC_{\text{LR}} \tag{4.48}$$

where C_{LR} is given by (4.30).

The relevant short-period total cost function is given by

$$C_{\text{SR}}^T = P_K K + P_L \left[\frac{Q}{AK^\alpha} \right]^{\frac{1}{\beta}} \tag{4.49}$$

where K is given by (4.45). It is said to be a "short-period" cost function, for the firm will produce each of the outputs Q_i, $i = 1, \dots, T$, at total costs given by (4.49). The scale of plant is fixed for the T-period cost minimisers.

We see then that a more relevant cost-minimisation procedure for firms yields a set of cost curves different from those implied by the traditional one-period cost-minimisation analysis. Full consideration of fixed capital will lead the firm to choose a different scale in the T-period analysis than in the one-period analysis. One-period cost minimisation would imply that the firm operated at E on C_{SR} whereas it would actually operate at a point like E_1 or E_2 on $C_{\text{SR}}^T(1)$ or $C_{\text{SR}}^T(2)$ (the relevant short-period cost function given by (4.49)) in figure 4.4 to produce an output of Q. If the observation is assumed to take place at the beginning of the planning period and it is assumed that the level of capital is fixed over T for the "one-period" cost minimiser as well as for the T-period cost minimiser then the total costs implied would be higher at this observed Q for the T-period cost minimiser. However, over the planning horizon output will fluctuate and total costs will be smaller than C_{SR} on $C_{\text{SR}}^T(1)$ for $Q > Q_2$ and on $C_{\text{SR}}^T(2)$ for $Q < Q_1$. The T-period cost-minimisation procedure simply determines the scale of plant.

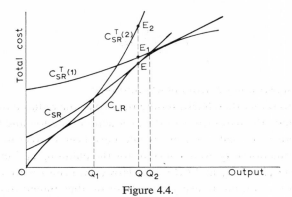

Figure 4.4.

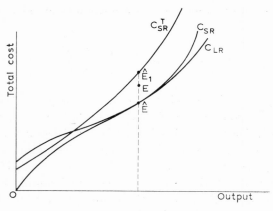

Figure 4.5.

Each firm, however, is observed to be at a point like E on figure 4.5 where both total costs and output are known. The estimation procedure followed by Nerlove determines parameters of the production function which places $\hat{E}$ (the estimate of E) on a one-period long-run total cost function. However the correct estimation procedure is to determine the parameters of the production function which imply that the firm operates on the T-period short-run total cost curve at $\hat{E}_1$ where

$$C_{SR}^T = \left(\sigma A^{-\frac{1}{\beta}}\right)^{\frac{\beta}{\alpha+\beta}} \left(\frac{P_L}{\beta}\right)^{\frac{\beta}{\alpha+\beta}} \left(\frac{P_K}{\alpha}\right)^{\frac{\alpha}{\alpha+\beta}} \left(\alpha + \beta \frac{Q^{\frac{1}{\beta}}}{\sigma}\right) \qquad (4.50)$$

where

$$\sigma = \frac{1}{T} \sum_{i=1}^{T} Q_i^{\frac{1}{\beta}}$$

derived by substituting K from (4.45) into (4.49).

Thus (4.50) rather than (4.30) should be used as the reduced form equation to estimate the parameters of the production function and hence the degree of returns to scale. Nerlove would have been correct in using the one-period function if Q_i were constant for the planning period; then, as we have seen $C_{LR}^T = TC_{LR}$ and $C_{SR}^T = C_{SR}$. However, firms do not operate at the same level of output in every period nor do they intend to do so.

The method of estimating the parameters of the production function from (4.50) would seem to be a formidable task and will not be discussed here.

Nerlove's estimates of the cost function did not produce a set of random residuals. True costs were underestimated at small and at high levels of output and overestimated at medium levels of output. He explains this in terms of the non-constancy of returns to scale over the full output range or by a variation of Friedman's permanent income hypothesis. Another explanation may be offered in terms of the criticism that we have made here.

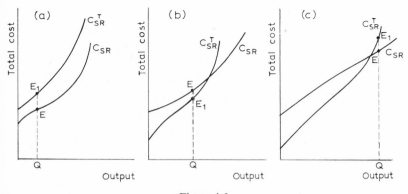

Figure 4.6.

Suppose that the diagrams in figure 4.6 are schematic representations of three typical firms that are observed to operate at "small", "medium" and "large" levels of output in (a), (b) and (c) respectively. C_{SR} is the implied short-run total cost curve derived from observations on each firm while C_{SR}^T is the relevant total cost curve for the size of plant observed when cost minimisation takes place over T periods.[48] From one-period analysis estimated costs would be at E while from T-period analysis estimated costs would be at E_1 for the observed output Q for each of the firms. If T-period analysis correctly represents the cost behaviour of entrepreneurs and the cost structures follow this schematic representation then this

---

[48] Note that estimated C_{SR} and C_{SR}^T need not have the same level of total fixed costs.

would provide an explanation for the pattern of residuals derived by Nerlove from his estimation procedure.[49]

Nerlove's study is interesting in that he assumes cost-minimisation behaviour on the part of entrepreneurs to derive a reduced form equation for estimating the parameters of the production function. But as we have seen, apart from any criticism of his work on the basis of no consideration of machine-mix or technological change, within the context of his methodology the cost-minimisation procedure he used is not the relevant one for firms in this industry. Thus too much weight cannot be given to his estimates of returns to scale in the production of electricity.

P. J. DHRYMES and M. KURZ[50]

Dhrymes and Kurz, in order to obtain measures of technological change and returns to scale in the steam-electric power industry of the United States, combined the methodology of Komiya and Nerlove. They divided their sample of plants into technological periods, and for plants of each vintage parameters of a production function were estimated from equations implied by an assumption concerning the cost-minimising behaviour of entrepreneurs.

The sample consisted of 362 newly constructed plants, built in the period 1937–59.[51] Generally each plant was included as an observation once only, in the year following construction of the plant. However, in a few cases a plant was included more than once when there was an increase of at least 50 per cent of capacity in the same technological period. The rationale given for single observations on a plant was to observe the plant at its "normal" level of operation, and a year was considered sufficiently long for a plants to achieve this level. This argument is similar to that of Barzel's,[52] and as we shall see the implication is that the firm when

---

[49] It should be noted that if Nerlove's model is correct his explanations regarding the pattern of residuals would be satisfactory. But if his model is incorrect, as is argued here, the above explanation of the pattern of residuals which he obtains, is only one possible explanation, and would have to be tested.

[50] Technology and Scale in Electricity Generation, *Econometrica* XXXII, July 1964, p. 287.

[51] A few plants initially built prior to 1937 were included in the sample where it seemed likely that old equipment was retired or used only for standby purposes so that effective operation was carried out by equipment built during the period of study.

[52] See p. 68, above.

observed operates at an optimum, in the sense of being on its long-run cost function.[53]

An analysis of data on plant operation, however, shows that the degree of capacity operation varies widely for plants in their first year of operation as well as over the life of plants. Thus it is doubtful that the operation of a plant in its first year of operation is at a "normal" level of capacity operation.

There is no consideration of the variation of plant output and input over different levels of capacity operation, nor is machine-mix of plants explicitly considered. It is likely, however, that this last objection is not too serious, for only about 50 of the plants had two or more generating units, and these were generally confined to plants with total capacity of 150 megawatts or more.

Unlike Komiya's analysis plants were not classified by vintage and fuel type but by vintage and size, where size was measured in installed megawatts. There was no differentiation with respect to fuel-input type but in the estimation of the labour-input function a differentiation of plants was introduced to account for electric plants of the outdoor type for which labour requirements could be expected to differ *a priori*.

The technological periods used were somewhat different from Komiya's, 1937–45, 1946–50, 1951–54 and 1955–59. A group of plants of capacity at least 450 MW, built between 1951 and 1959, were combined into one vintage-size cell. For each of the vintage-size cells a function was estimated derived from assumptions concerning the behaviour of entrepreneurs and the assumed production function.

The form of production function assumed by Dhrymes and Kurz was the ACMS function,[54]

$$Q = A \left[\alpha_F F^{\beta_F} + \alpha_K K^{\beta_K} + \alpha_L L^{\beta_L} \right]^{\frac{1}{\gamma}} \qquad (4.51)$$

where Q, F, K and L are output and fuel, capital and labour input respectively, per unit time period. Subsequent analysis, however, led to the abandonment of this model because of the particular nature of labour

---

[53] Dhrymes and Kurz, *op. cit.*, footnote 11, p. 298.
[54] Arrow, Minhas, Chenery and Solow: (4.51) is also referred to as the CES or SMAC production function.

input, and it was replaced by

$$Q = \min \left[g(L), (\alpha_F F^{\beta_F} + \alpha_K K^{\beta_K})^{\frac{1}{\gamma}} \right]. \tag{4.52}$$

The interpretation of (4.52) is that to produce an output Q a quantity $g^{-1}(Q)$ of labour is required. Thus there are only substitution possibilities between fuel and capital. This production process is considered by Dhrymes and Kurz as an ex-ante production function in the sense that it expresses the substitution possibilities before a plant is installed.

The model (4.52) is not estimated directly. Following Nerlove it is assumed that entrepreneurs are faced with exogenous demands and thus given factor prices they minimise total cost. The estimation procedure then implies, that given output, inputs and input prices, the parameters of the production function are estimated on the basis of this cost-minimisation procedure. No optimisation can take place with respect to labour because of the assumed fixed coefficient of labour input given in (4.52), thus cost minimisation can only take place with respect to fuel and capital inputs. The implied factor demand equations are then used as estimating functions to determine the parameters of the production function.

Entrepreneurs are assumed to follow the following optimisation procedure: minimise total fuel and capital cost (4.53) for a given output, fuel and capital price, subject to the restraint imposed by the production function (4.54).

$$C = P_K K + P_F F, \tag{4.53}$$

$$Q = A \left[\alpha_F F^{\beta_F} + \alpha_K K^{\beta_K} \right]^{\frac{1}{\gamma}}. \tag{4.54}$$

The solution of this problem leads to the following demand equations for fuel and capital respectively.[55]

$$\log F = \frac{1}{\beta_F - 1} \log \frac{\alpha_K \beta_K}{\alpha_F \beta_F} + \frac{1}{\beta_F - 1} \log \frac{P_F}{P_K} + \frac{\beta_K - 1}{\beta_F - 1} \log K \tag{4.55}$$

---

[55] (4.56) is obtained by estimating a function for $\log K$ similar to (4.55) and then substituting for F from the production function.

$$\log K = \frac{1}{\beta_K - 1} \log \frac{\alpha_F \beta_F}{\alpha_K \beta_K} + \frac{1}{\beta_K - 1} \log \frac{P_K}{P_F} + \frac{\beta_F - 1}{\beta_F(\beta_K - 1)}$$

$$\times \log\left[\frac{1}{\alpha_F}\left(\frac{Q}{A}\right)^\gamma - \frac{\alpha_K K^{\beta_K}}{\alpha_F}\right]. \quad (4.56)$$

If (4.56) can be solved explicitly for K in terms of Q and P_K/P_F which is exogenous then we derive an estimating function for K,

$$\log K = G\left[\log Q, \log \frac{P_K}{P_F}\right]. \quad (4.57)$$

If (4.57) is estimated then $\log \widehat{K}$ may be substituted for $\log K$ in (4.55), and (4.55) may then be estimated by ordinary least squares. This is simply the use of two-stage least squares to estimate the coefficients of (4.55).

One problem is that (4.56) cannot easily be solved explicitly for K so that it is assumed that (4.56) is approximated by

$$\log K = a_0 + a_1 \frac{P_K}{P_F} + a_2 \log Q. \quad (4.58)$$

The procedure followed by Dhrymes and Kurz is first to estimate a function of the form (4.58), then substitute the estimate $\log \widehat{K}$ in (4.55), and finally estimate (4.55) by ordinary least squares. The shortcomings of using (4.58) to approximate (4.56) are fully recognised.

The implied estimates of α_F, α_K, β_F and β_K are obtained [56] by estimating (4.55) at the second stage of two-stage least squares together with a normalisation procedure

$$\alpha_F \alpha_K = 1 \quad (4.59)$$

imposed on the production function. A and γ are then estimated by substituting $\hat{\alpha}_F$, $\hat{\alpha}_K$, $\hat{\beta}_F$, $\hat{\beta}_K$ in (4.54) and estimating

$$\log Z = a + b \log Q \quad (4.60)$$

---

[56] Dhrymes and Kurz, *op. cit.*, p. 295.

by ordinary least squares, where

$$Z = \hat{\alpha}_F F^{\beta_F} + \hat{\alpha}_K K^{\beta_K}. \tag{4.61}$$

The use of two-stage least squares is interesting but the approximation of (4.56) by (4.58) must be borne in mind.

The major objection to this procedure of cost minimisation is similar to that raised against Nerlove's assumption concerning the optimal behaviour of entrepreneurs in the steam-electric power industry. If for plants output is exogenous, then a cost-minimisation procedure on the part of entrepreneurs is appropriate, but this will be in dynamic terms rather than one-period terms assumed by Nerlove and by Dhrymes and Kurz in their study. The estimation procedure used by Nerlove and by Dhrymes and Kurz derives parameters of the production function on the assumption that the plant operates on the long-run total cost function of traditional micro-economic analysis.[57] The correct estimation procedure would be based on the behavioral assumption that entrepreneurs min-imise cost over a planning period during which capital is fixed, so that the plant operates on a cost curve derived from a consideration of planned outputs over time.

Let us consider the correct approach to this problem when it is assumed that the ex-ante production function is the ACMS function used in this study, and the length of the planning horizon is T unit periods. The cost-minimisation procedure adopted implies the minimisation of

$$Z = P_F \sum_{i=1}^{T} F_i + T P_K K + \sum_{i=1}^{T} \lambda_i [Q_i - Q] \tag{4.62}$$

where the λ_i are lagrangian multipliers and Q is given by (4.54). Factor prices are assumed constant over time and for simplicity no discount factor is introduced. First order conditions are given by

$$\frac{\partial Z}{\partial K} = T P_K - \sum_{i=1}^{T} \lambda_i \frac{\partial Q}{\partial K}\bigg|_{F = F_i} = 0, \tag{4.63}$$

---

[57] Here is the need for Dhrymes and Kurz to assume that in the year after construction a plant operates at its "normal" level of output, i.e. where the short-run total cost curve relating to the scale of plant observed is tangent to the long-run total cost function.

$$\frac{\partial Z}{\partial F_i} = P_F - \lambda_i \frac{\partial Q}{\partial F}\bigg|_{F=F_i} = 0 \qquad i = 1, ..., T, \qquad (4.64)$$

$$\frac{\partial Z}{\partial \lambda_i} = Q_i - Q = 0 \qquad i = 1, ..., T. \qquad (4.65)$$

From (4.64) we have

$$\lambda_i = P_F \left(\frac{\partial Q}{\partial F}\bigg|_{F=F_i}\right)^{-1} \qquad i = 1, ..., T \qquad (4.66)$$

and for the ACMS production function

$$\frac{\dfrac{\partial Q}{\partial K}}{\dfrac{\partial Q}{\partial F}} = \frac{\beta_K \alpha_K K^{\beta_K - 1}}{\beta_F \alpha_F F^{\beta_F - 1}}. \qquad (4.67)$$

Then substituting for λ_i in (4.63) and using (4.67) we have

$$TP_K - P_F \frac{\beta_K \alpha_K}{\beta_F \alpha_F} K^{\beta_K - 1} \sum_{i=1}^{T} F_i^{1-\beta_F} = 0. \qquad (4.68)$$

Solving for K and taking logarithms we have

$$\log K = \frac{1}{\beta_K - 1} \log \frac{P_K}{P_F} + \frac{1}{\beta_K - 1} \log \frac{\beta_F \alpha_F}{\beta_K \alpha_K} + \frac{1}{\beta_K - 1} \log T \left[\sum_{i=1}^{T} F_i^{1-\beta_F}\right]^{-1}.$$

$$(4.69)$$

This equation is similar to (4.55) except that the consequences of a T-period planning horizon are expressed in a form of weighted average of the fuel inputs. If each F_i is constant then this would reduce to one-period cost minimisation.[58] The F_i are endogenous and appear in (4.69) in an awkward manner which makes the estimation of this equation by a

---

[58] With constant capital and F_i this implies that planned output is the same in each period.

process of two-stage least squares difficult. A suggestion will be given out-lining a possible estimation procedure.

From the production function (4.54) we have

$$F_i^{1-\beta_F} = \left\{ \alpha_F^{1-\frac{1}{\beta_F}} \left[\left(\frac{Q_i}{A} \right)^{\frac{1}{\gamma}} - \alpha_K K^{\beta_K} \right] \right\}^{\frac{1}{\beta_F}-1} \qquad i = 1, ..., T \quad (4.70)$$

If we substitute for K from (4.69) in each of these T equations we have a set of functions

$$H\left[F_i^{1-\beta_F}, Q_i, P_K, P_F \right] = 0 \qquad i = 1, ..., T. \qquad (4.71)$$

If each of these H functions can be explicitly solved for $F_i^{1-\beta_F}$ to give

$$F_i^{1-\beta_F} = G\left[Q_i, P_K, P_F \right] \qquad i = 1, ..., T \qquad (4.72)$$

we could sum these over T and obtain

$$\sum_{i=1}^{T} F_i^{1-\beta_F} = \psi\left[Q_1, Q_2, ..., Q_T, P_K, P_F \right]. \qquad (4.73)$$

If we have an independent estimate of β_F then (4.73) may be estimated by ordinary least squares for the plants in our sample and the estimate of the dependent variable substituted in (4.69). Thus (4.69) may now be estimated by ordinary least squares to complete the two-stage estimation procedure. The difficulty with this approach is that an independent estimate of β_F would seem to be necessary and an explicit function like (4.73) may not be able to be obtained without approximation procedures.[59]

---

[59] Given this independent estimate of β_F we could also use (4.72) as the estimating equation at the first stage of two-stage least squares with a combination of time series and cross-section data. Or use β_F directly in (4.69) and use (4.72) in the form

$$F_i = G^{\frac{1}{1-\beta_F}}$$

as the first stage of two-stage least squares, again with a combination of time series and cross-section data.

We see then that a correct formulation of the cost-minimisation procedure for plants in the electric-power industry, taking into consideration the fixed nature of capital, leads to factor demand functions which depend on the exogenous outputs of the T-period planning horizon. The estimation procedure as well as the forms of the functions involved is very different from that implied by the assumption of one-period cost minimisation. It would seem that a full consideration of the estimation procedure based on a hypothesis of T-period cost minimisation is more difficult for the ACMS than the Cobb–Douglas production function, and it will not be further discussed in this study. Only if observed output in the first full year of operation is the planned output for each of the T periods, will the estimating procedure used by Dhrymes and Kurz be equivalent to an estimating procedure based on a T-period planning horizon.

The measure of capital input used represented capital services, a flow rather than a stock measure of capital. For each plant the number of installed megawatts was multiplied by the sum of hours hot and connected to load and hours hot but not connected to load. Thus capital for Dhrymes and Kurz is measured in megawatthours. However, as we have seen (chapter 3), a machine does not necessarily operate at full capacity in each hour of generation and when it operates not connected to load instantaneous output is zero. A more significant measure of the flow of capital services over the year in terms of the analysis employed by Dhrymes and Kurz would be the aggregate of installed megawatts multiplied by the degree of capacity utilisation in each hour.

The model initially estimated, (4.51), included labour, but the results obtained for the labour equation were not successful because labour is not a substitute for capital and fuel in the production of electricity. To estimate labour requirements from (4.52), the function

$$\log L = \log B + a_1 Z_1 + a_2 Z_2 + \log Q \qquad (4.74)$$

was fitted to plants of each vintage, but no differentiation was made for the size classification used in the fuel equation. Z_1 and Z_2 are dummy variables relating to geographical areas, B is a constant, Q is output and L is labour input. The dummy variables determine the shift in the constant term of (4.74). The results of this fitted equation showed uniformly increasing returns to scale to labour which was constant over the technological periods considered. The effect of technology on the constant terms of (4.74) is significant, although not quite uniform over all the technological periods, which shows the reduced labour requirements for improved technology. Labour requirements varied significantly for different geographical regions, with plants in the Southern Pacific Coast and the South, usually of the outdoor type, needing less labour than plants in other areas.

This study by Dhrymes and Kurz is interesting in that it uses the ACMS production function as the model from which the behavioral relations are derived. The use of two-stage least squares necessitates an approximation for a function relating capital input to exogenous variables. We have seen that the cost-minimising behaviour assumed for entrepreneurs is static and will only be relevant to entrepreneurial behaviour if the observed level of operation is the planned level for each year of the planning horizon.[60] There is no consideration of machine-mix of plants in this study nor of the degree of capacity utilisation of plants.

4.4. Summary

This survey shows the variety of approaches to the measurement of production and cost relations in the steam-electric power industry. The earlier approaches of Nordin, Lomax and Johnston were succeeded by the more sophisticated analyses of Komiya and Barzel and the "behaviourists" Nerlove, and Dhrymes and Kurz. The general criticisms stated at the beginning of this chapter, in addition to criticisms of the methods employed by the various authors, provide sufficient justification for the empirical study of the production process in the steam-electric power industry which follows.

---

[60] Even if the T-period production plan assumes that output is to be constant in each period, thus dictating a particular plant scale, there is no guarantee that planned output is realised in the first year of operation, so that the plant may not be operating on its long-run total cost function.

Appendix

SUILIN LING[61]

Ling's study was received after the survey and critique of chapter 4 was completed, and we shall briefly discuss it in this appendix.

His work falls into the second category: studies which assume optimal behaviour on the part of entrepreneurs. What makes his work particularly interesting is the combination of engineering information and economic theory from which are obtained cost curves for steam-electric generating systems, and hence the measurement of scale economies in relation to these cost curves. His technique proceeds in four steps:

(1) Secular trends in steam conditions (pressure and temperature) and maximum capacity of installed turbines are combined with engineering considerations to derive a relationship between station heat rate (fuel input) and unit scale. This is analogous to the ex-post production function of chapter 5.

(2) A basic system of size 2500 MW with a fixed machine-mix[62] is assumed. Annual costs of generation are calculated for this system for varying degrees of capacity utilisation. Cost data is taken from trade sources and maintenance periods, and forced outage is allowed for. Engineering information is used to distribute output over the units in the plant.

The system is now assumed to expand from 2500 MW to 13700 MW by an optimum system expansion pattern developed by electricity engineers. At various system sizes between 2500 MW and 13700 MW annual costs of generation are calculated for several system load factors as they were for the static model.

The result of these calculations is a set of data constructed from ex-ante engineering considerations and which relates to systems of between 2500 MW and 13700 MW which operate at varying system loads.

(3) This data is used to fit average cost functions. A Cobb–Douglas function is fitted but the following form gives better results:[63]

$$C_a = kS^n \eta^{m + p \ln \eta}$$

[61] *Economies of Scale in the Steam-Electric Power Generating Industry.* Amsterdam: North Holland Publishing Company, 1964.

[62] 10 units of 50 MW, 12 units of 100 MW and 4 units of 200 MW.

[63] Ling, *op. cit.*, pp. 47–48. Total and marginal cost curves are also calculated.

where C_a = annual average generating cost in mills per kWh,

    η = system load factor in per cent,

    S = system installed capacity in megawatts,

and $k = 5534$, $n = -0.1688$, $m = -1.8406$, $p = 0.1428$ are the estimated values of the parameters; $\bar{R} = 0.999$. The importance of economies of scale is seen in the value of n, which shows that average generating costs decrease as the size of system increases, for any given system load factor. (4) Ling fully realizes that his fitted cost functions depend on data derived ex-ante from engineering considerations and from his assumed basic system and method of expansion. He goes on to see whether the cost functions he has calculated fit data for four utility systems operating in the United States between 1938 and 1958. He finds that his functions perform well using this ex-post data.

Ling is not concerned explicitly with the differentiation of the effects of technological change and changes in scale. Since secular changes in steam conditions are related to secular increases in unit scale, his measures of scale economies are compounded with changes in technology. Thus his cost functions are the resultants of movements along and movements of the production function. Nevertheless, his approach is extremely interesting and seems to provide a good explanation of the movement of costs in steam-electric power generation.

CHAPTER 5

THE EX-POST PRODUCTION FUNCTION, SCALE ECONOMIES AND TECHNOLOGICAL CHANGE IN STEAM-ELECTRIC POWER GENERATION

In this chapter the results of an analysis of the ex-post production function for steam-electric power generation are presented. The ideas expressed in chapters 2 and 3 concerning the operation of a multi-unit plant, which are relevant for this industry, are applied here. The turbine-generator unit with its associated boilers and ancillary equipment – the machine – is the basic unit of observation. Each of these machines is characterised by a measure of size and vintage, and the effects of changes in scale and technology on the production process are reflected in the different ex-post production functions for different machines. These effects of changes in scale and technology are separated and quantified, and the degree of capacity utilisation of machines is explicitly considered. In order to perform this analysis, the problem of using annual data to estimate the parameters of an essentially instantaneous production process must first be solved.

5.1. Description of the sample and data

The source of data on plant operation is the series "Steam-Electric Plant Construction Cost and Annual Production Expenses" (the FPC Reports), published by the Federal Power Commission first for the year 1938 and annually since.[1] This is a unique source of statistics relating to input and output data on a plant-by-plant basis. The coverage of these reports has increased over the years. In 1938 the plants reported comprised some 59 per cent of installed capacity and 75 per cent of output of steam-electric plants in the United States.[2] By 1953, the last year of the sample,

---

[1] See Appendix A.

[2] *FPC Report 1962–63*, Table 2, p. xix.

these figures increased to 79 per cent and 88 per cent respectively.[3] Data
are published on output and inputs in both physical and money form for
labour, capital and fuel. The overall plant factor and hours of operation,
hot and connected, hot and not connected, and cold are reported. The
breakdown of hours, however, was reported only until 1953, which has
necessitated the limitation of the sample to years of operation between
1938 and 1953.

Detailed information is also given on the machine-mix of plants in
terms of size and vintage of turbine-generator units in place, and changes
in the machine-mix which take place over time are also reported. New
plants are fully covered and details of their physical capital structure are
likewise given.

There are three major shortcomings of the data which have necessitated
the approximations discussed in chapter 3. First, data on inputs and output are published on an overall plant basis with no direct observations of
operations on a single machine, unless plants have only one turbine
generator. Secondly, observations are on an annual basis which is not the
same period as that of the production operation. And thirdly, the measure
of labour input used is "average number of employees" in a plant during
the year, which is a poor measure of labour input. Despite these shortcomings, however, the data seem adequate for estimates of the production
process.

Before proceeding to a discussion of the sample, a word should be said
about the adjustment of the published fuel-input data to obtain a measure
of fuel input per kilowatthour for each machine in a plant, when hours
hot but not connected to load are allowed for. In chapter 3, pp. 42–44,
and equation (3.23) this adjustment procedure is outlined. However, the
application of this adjustment to data did not significantly alter the figure
of fuel input so that the published B (equation (3.18) p. 42) was taken as a
measure of fuel input for each machine in a plant and no adjustment was
made. An example of this adjustment is given in table 5.1.

The greatest percentage adjustment is for 1938 which is 2.3 per cent.
In addition the measure a_K, input of fuel per kilowatthour at capacity,
cannot be observed directly but was taken to be the observed B for the
greatest PF*, where PF* is the correct measure of capacity utilisation

---

[3] *FPC Report 1953*, p. iv.

TABLE 5.1

Example of the fuel adjustment calculation.
Plant: Minnesota valley 2 × 10 MW machines

Year	B	$\left(\dfrac{1}{PF}\right)\left(\dfrac{t_2}{T}\right)(0.01 a_K)$	B^*	t_2
	(1)	(2)	(3) = (1) − (2)	(4)
1938	16 349	378	15 971	3 655
1939	16 290	233	16 057	3 007
1940	15 608	138	15 470	2 087
1941	15 955	60	15 895	903
1942	15 788	113	15 675	1 575
1943	15 754	85	15 669	1 368
1944	15 919	141	15 778	1 901
1945	16 215	150	16 065	1 940
1946	16 064	105	15 959	1 807
1947	16 330	51	16 279	1 370
1948	16 289	50	16 239	1 537
1949	16 037	35	16 002	877

Note: Columns (1), (2) and (3) are in BTU's per kilowatthour; Column (4) is hours
when plant operates hot but not connected to load during the year.

(see p. 41). For the plant of table 5.1 this greatest PF* was 68.6 per cent.
Thus if input of fuel per kilowatthour falls as capacity is approached, the
a_K used in the adjustment of column (2) is an overestimate of the true a_K,
and the true B^* is greater than the calculated B^*. It would seem then,
that an adjustment of the published B to allow for hours hot but not
connected to load alters the data only slightly so that if no adjustments
were made the estimates would not be significantly impaired. Further, in
any given year only a proportion of the plants operate hot but not connected so that even the small adjustment implied is not applicable to
every B.

The sample was chosen to include only those plants which had turbine
generators of the same size and vintage, but between plants in the sample
the size and vintage of machines vary. A plant was included in the sample
from its first full year of operation until 1953 or until units of a different
size and/or vintage were added to the plant. Information on the charac-

TABLE 5.2
Number of years of observation and plants in the sample

Vintage	Coal		Non-coal		Mixed	
	observations	plants	observations	plants	observations	plants
1920–24	37	3	0	0	0	0
1925–29	121	10	62	6	25	3
1930–34	6	1	21	4	0	0
1935–39	91	9	75	7	32	3
1940–44	49	9	41	7	10	1
1945–50	103	29	34	11	49	19
1951–53	12	9	37	22	7	5

teristics of machines added to a plant is published in the FPC Reports and a plant was retained in the sample if the added turbines were of the same size as existing machines in the plant and if they seemed of the same vintage in terms of the published characteristics. The years of operation covered in the sample, which included plants of machine vintages from 1920 to 1953, were from 1938 to 1953. The year of installation of a machine was taken to be its vintage, i.e., the index of the degree of technological change embodied in machines.

The plants were stratified by vintage and fuel type initially, as shown in table 5.2. A coal plant is one which could burn only coal as fuel, a non-coal plant is one which had no coal-burning equipment, while a mixed plant is one which had equipment to burn coal and either oil or gas or both. Some 812 observations were made on 158 different plants. The sample is complete in terms of the available information published in the FPC Reports.

5.2. The ex-post production function and a temporal aggregation problem

In order to estimate the ex-post production function for machines, the problem of using annual plant data for individual machines had to be solved. In chapter 3 measures of capacity utilisation and fuel input for individual machines were derived and it is stated that the particular form of these measures is due partly to the solution of the problem of using annual data to estimate an essentially instantaneous production relation.[4] We shall now consider this problem which is in fact one form of the "aggregation problem".

For simplicity suppose that there is a production process which has a period of production of length Δt and such that an output q_{it} is produced using only one input x_{it} on machine i at time t. Thus the process production function for the ith machine may be written as

$$q_{it} = f(x_{it}) \tag{5.1}$$

where it is assumed that only machines of the same vintage are considered so that they have identical production functions.

However, observations on this process are taken over time intervals of length $\Delta T > \Delta t$, and the observed input and output for the ith machine are given by X_{iT} and Q_{iT} respectively. The problem is to determine whether a function F exists such that if (5.2) is estimated, the coefficients of F will be simple functions of the coefficients of (5.1), so that the coefficients of (5.1) may be obtained from those of (5.2). Thus this problem may be stated as how to use T-period data to estimate a t-period process.

$$Q_{iT} = F(X_{iT}) \tag{5.2}$$

More generally we may consider the choice of aggregate variables Q_{iT} and X_{iT}, given by (5.3) and (5.4), such that the choice of the functional form F in (5.2) together with (5.3) and (5.4), will enable the coefficients of (5.1) to be derived from the coefficients of the estimated function (5.2). However, the range of choice of Q_{iT} and X_{iT} in (5.3) and (5.4) will be limited by the nature of T-period data.

$$Q_{iT} = \theta_1(q_{i1}, ..., q_{iT}) \tag{5.3}$$

$$X_{iT} = \theta_2(x_{i1}, ..., x_{iT}) \tag{5.4}$$

Let us now consider the application of these ideas to the estimation of the ex-post production function for the steam-electric power industry. The objective is to derive a functional form for the ex-post production func-

---

4 See p. 37.

tion which, as well as making economic sense, enables annual data to be used to estimate an essentially instantaneous process. Suppose then, that for the ith machine in a vintage fuel-type cell of table 5.2 we may write the ex-post production function as

$$a_{it} = g\left(\frac{X_{it}}{X_{iK}}, X_{iK}\right) \qquad (5.5)$$

where a_{it} is the input of fuel per kilowatt/Δt, X_{it}/X_{iK} is the degree of capacity utilisation during the interval t and X_{iK} is the size of the machine in megawatts. Equation (5.5) is identical to equation (3.1) of chapter 3 except that we now explicitly identify the machine. The function g in (5.5) will vary according to the vintage and fuel-type characteristics of the machine i, but we consider only one of the fuel-type vintage cells of table 5.2 so that for all machines in this cell the function (5.5) is identical.

The period of observation on any machine, ΔT, is the year, with the data on fuel input and output actually referring to the period during the year when the machine operates hot and connected to load. Thus we have for each machine annual data with which to estimate an essentially instantaneous production process. For purposes of exposition the process time period, Δt, may be considered as one hour in length.

Before proceeding, however, it should be stated that in each vintage fuel-type cell the observations are a mixture of cross-section and time series data. In any year of observation in a vintage fuel-type cell there is a cross-section of observation on machines, and for each machine in each cell there will be a time series of observations. It will be shown that this combination of time series and cross-section data complicates the analysis of the aggregation problem we are considering.

However, first we shall assume that only one machine is being considered. How then for a single machine can annual data be used to estimate an hourly process? As an illustration suppose that (5.5) may be expressed in Cobb–Douglas form (5.6), where v_{it} is an error term which may be explained as due to random elements between machines or differences in the efficiency of machine operators.

$$a_{it} = A\left(\frac{X_{it}}{X_{iK}}\right)^{\alpha} (X_{iK})^{\beta} e^{v_{it}}. \qquad (5.6)$$

The error term v_{it} is a stochastic variable which is assumed to have the following properties:

$$E(v_{it}) = 0 \quad \left.\vphantom{\begin{matrix}a\\b\end{matrix}}\right\} \quad t = 1, \ldots, T \qquad (5.7)$$
$$E(v_{it}^2) = \sigma_i^2 \qquad (5.8)$$

$$E(v_{ir}v_{is}) = 0 \quad \left\{\begin{matrix} r \neq s \\ r, s = 1, \cdots, T \end{matrix}\right. \qquad (5.9)$$

Let M_{it} and X_{it} be respectively the total fuel input and output during the tth hour on the ith machine, then simple aggregates, M_{iT} and X_{iT} are given by (5.10) and (5.11), where it must be remembered that aggregation over the year is for only those hours when the machine operates hot and connected to load.

$$M_{iT} = \sum_{T_1} M_{it} \qquad (5.10)$$

$$X_{iT} = \sum_{T_1} X_{it} \qquad (5.11)$$

T_1 is the number of hours during the year when the machine is hot and connected to load. Let a_{iT} be input of fuel per kilowatthour over the hours hot and connected during T, then we have,

$$a_{iT} = \frac{M_{iT}}{X_{iT}} = \sum_{T_1} a_{it} w_{it} \qquad (5.12)$$

where

$$w_{it} = \frac{X_{it}}{\sum_{T_1} X_{it}} = \frac{X_{it}}{X_{iT}}. \qquad (5.13)$$

The T-period equation (5.12) may be written out fully in (5.14). The independent variable a_{iT} may be obtained from the published data but the form of (5.14) is not amenable to any straightforward estimation procedure and the X_{it} are not reported.

$$a_{iT} = \sum_{T_1} A \left(\frac{X_{it}}{X_{iK}}\right)^\alpha (X_{iK})^\beta w_{it} e^{v_{it}} \qquad (5.14)$$

As a second illustration suppose that the ex-post production function is postulated as being of the form[5]

$$a_{it} = \alpha \frac{X_{it}}{X_{iK}} + \beta X_{iK} + \gamma + v_{it} \qquad (5.15)$$

where v_{it} has the properties specified in (5.7), (5.8) and (5.9), and γ, α and β are the parameters to be estimated. Then by straightforward aggregation as in (5.12) we have that

$$a_{iT} = \sum_{T_1} \left(\alpha \left(\frac{X_{it}}{X_{iK}} \right) + \beta X_{iK} + \gamma + v_{it} \right) w_{it} \qquad (5.16)$$

$$\therefore a_{iT} = \alpha \frac{\sum\limits_{T_1} X_{it}^2}{X_{iK} X_{iT}} + \beta X_{iK} + \gamma + \sum_{T_1} w_{it} v_{it}$$

where w_{it} is defined by (5.13). Apart from problems concerned with the weighted error term, $\sum_{T_1} w_{it} v_{it}$, there is no method of obtaining the first independent variable from published data so that the parameters of (5.15) cannot be obtained from T-period data.

There are, however, two forms of the ex-post production function which, as well as being sensible *a priori*, may enable T-period data to be used to estimate the t-period parameters.

Consider first that in any vintage fuel-type cell we have data for the years $T_1, ..., T_s$ where in any year, say T_j, we have data on the set of machines $[M_j]$. In general a machine will not appear in all of the cross sections referring to the years $T_1, ..., T_s$. Suppose that we are interested in estimating an ex-post production function from the cross section for

---

[5] If (5.15) were estimated for a single machine, which of course has X_{iK} constant, the moment matrix would be singular and the estimation procedure would break down unless (5.15) were forced through the origin. However, a combination of time series and cross-section data implies that although the variable X_{iK} is constant for the ith machine it varies over machines. See E. KUH, *Capital Stock Growth: A Micro-Econometric Approach*, Amsterdam: North-Holland Publishing Company, 1963, p. 161, where Kuh describes X_{iK} as a "section variable". This note applies also to the models which follow.

year T_j. Consider the following models

$$a_{it} = \alpha \left(\frac{X_{it}}{X_{iK}}\right)^{-1} + \beta X_{iK} + \gamma + v_{it} \qquad \text{Model A} \quad (5.17)$$

and

$$a_{it} = \alpha \left(\frac{X_{it}}{X_{iK}}\right)^{-1} + \beta (X_{iK})^{-1} + \gamma + v_{it} \quad \text{Model B} \quad (5.18)$$

where a_{it}, X_{iK}, X_{it} are defined as before and refer to the ith machine in the set $[M_j]$ for which we have observations in the cross section of year T_j. The error term v_{it} is assumed to have the properties of (5.7), (5.8) and (5.9), and in addition we may postulate that

$$\sigma_i^2 = \sigma^2 \qquad (5.19)$$

for all machines in the set $[M_j]$. This property may be termed "cross-section t-period homoscedasticity".

Then if we perform the aggregation procedure of (5.12) on each of the machines in $[M_j]$ we have the following T-period functions, where T_{1ij} is the number of hours that machine i operates hot and connected to load during the year j, and a_{iT_j} is the input of fuel per kilowatthour for machine i during the year j. For model A

$$a_{iT_j} = \alpha \left(\frac{X_{iT_j}}{T_{1ij}X_{iK}}\right)^{-1} + \beta X_{iK} + \gamma + \sum_{T_{1ij}} v_{it}w_{it} \qquad (5.20)$$

and for model B

$$a_{iT_j} = \alpha \left(\frac{X_{iT_j}}{T_{1ij}X_{iK}}\right)^{-1} + \beta (X_{iK})^{-1} + \gamma + \sum_{T_{1ij}} v_{it}w_{it} \qquad (5.21)$$

where

$$w_{it} = \frac{X_{it}}{\sum_{T_{1ij}} X_{it}} \qquad (5.22)$$

and

$$X_{iT_j} = \sum_{T_{1ij}} X_{it}. \qquad (5.23)$$

The T-period models (5.20) and (5.21) developed from the t-period models are relations between variables which may be obtained from the annual plant data published in the FPC Reports.[6] The first independent variable on the right-hand side is simply the inverse of PF*[7] (the adjusted plant factor) which is a measure of the capacity operation of the machine over the year, and a_{iT_j} is identical to B^* of equation (3.24) of chapter 3 above. It would seem then, that an estimate of (5.20) or (5.21) on a cross-section basis within a fuel-type vintage cell would provide estimates of α, β and γ. But first it is necessary to consider the properties of the aggregated error term (5.24) to determine whether the estimation of (5.20) and (5.21) by ordinary least squares from the observations on $[M_j]$, is valid. The weighted error term in (5.20) and (5.21) is

$$V_{iTj} = \sum_{T_{1ij}} v_{it} w_{it} \quad \text{for the } i\text{th machine in } [M_j]. \tag{5.24}$$

We have then that

$$E(V_{iTj}) = 0 \quad \text{for all machines in } [M_j], \text{ and for } j = 1, \ldots, s, \tag{5.25}$$

and using (5.19) that

$$\text{Var}(V_{iTj}) = \sigma^2 \frac{\sum_{T_{1ij}} X_{it}^2}{[\sum_{T_{1ij}} X_{it}]^2} \quad \text{for the } i\text{th machine in } [M_j]. \tag{5.26}$$

Also, for the hth and ith machines in the cross section for year T_j,

$$\text{Cov}[V_{hTj}V_{iTj}] = E[V_{hTj}V_{iTj}] = E[\sum_{T_{1hj}} v_{ht} w_{ht} \sum_{T_{1ij}} v_{it} w_{it}] = 0 \tag{5.27}$$

provided that for any two machines in the set $[M_j]$

$$E(v_{ht_h} v_{it_i}) = 0 \quad \text{for } \begin{cases} t_h = 1, \ldots, T_{1hj} \\ t_i = 1, \ldots, T_{1ij} \end{cases} \tag{5.28}$$

(5.28) is plausible since the machines are in separate plants.

---

[6] See chapter 3.

[7] See chapter 3. Here T_{1ij} is equivalent to t_1 of the notation of chapter 3.

However, just considering the cross-section of year T_j, equation (5.26) implies that although there is cross-section t-period homoscedasticity, there is cross-section T-period heteroscedasticity. Thus if (5.20) or (5.21) were estimated from the cross-section data on the set $[M_j]$ by ordinary least squares, the estimates of the parameters would be unbiased and consistent but the presence of heteroscedasticity would mean that there is a loss of efficiency.[8] If the X_{it} were observed the data could be adjusted to allow for T-period heteroscedasticity by using Aitken's generalisation of ordinary least squares. But if these hourly output figures were recorded models A and B could be estimated directly and there would be no need to use T-period functions.

It would seem then that an estimation of (5.20) or (5.21) from the cross section $[M_j]$ would result in a loss of efficiency. However, it is possible to make certain assumptions which if plausible would imply that heteroscedasticity is not present. If we assumed that for the year T_j the term

$$\frac{\sum\limits_{T_{1ij}} X_{it}^2}{[\sum\limits_{T_{1ij}} X_{it}]^2} = A_j \tag{5.29}$$

for all machines in the set $[M_j]$, we have from (5.26) that

$$\text{var}\,(V_{iTj}) = \sigma^2 A_j \tag{5.30}$$

so that in the cross section, t-period homoscedasticity results in T-period homoscedasticity.[9] There is no *a priori* reason why (5.29) should hold however, but if it does hold (5.29) in conjunction with (5.25) and (5.27) are sufficient to enable (5.20) or (5.21) to be estimated by ordinary least squares from any cross section in a vintage fuel-type cell and to ensure that the estimated parameters are best linear unbiassed estimates.

To repeat then, on the basis of the assumptions made here it is possible

---

[8] For example see J. JOHNSTON, *Econometric Methods*, New York: McGraw-Hill Book Company, 1963, p. 211.

[9] The implications of cross section t-period heteroscedasticity in the aggregation problem will not be pursued in this study. It is plausible that there is t-period heteroscedasticity such that $\text{Var}(v_{it}) = f(X_{it})\,\sigma^2$, or perhaps, $\text{Var}(v_{it}) = g(X_{iK})\,\sigma^2$.

to obtain best linear unbiassed estimates of the parameters of (5.20) and
(5.21) and hence of model A or model B, for all cross sections in each of
the vintage fuel-type cells of table 5.2. However, there is a combination of
time series and cross-section data in each of these cells. The question then
arises of what additional assumptions would have to be made in order
that the models (5.20) and (5.21) could be estimated by ordinary least
squares from a combination of time series and cross-section data in any
cell, as well as from any cross section, and such that there would be no
loss of efficiency due to heteroscedasticity.

In each of the years $T_1, ..., T_s$ for a cell, we have in general observations
on a different set of machines $[M_j], j = 1, ..., s$. Applying the assumptions
used above we have derived cross-section T-period homoscedasticity. In
order to derive general homoscedasticity in a cell it would be necessary
for the variance in (5.30) to be constant over cross sections. For this to be
so the properties of the t-period error term given in (5.7), (5.8) and (5.9)
together with the condition (5.19) must be identical for each cross section
in a vintage fuel-type cell. Also we must have that

$$A_j = A_k \qquad j, k = 1, ..., s \qquad (5.30a)$$

where A_j is given by (5.29). Further, to ensure the independence of error
terms between cross sections it would be necessary that

$$\text{Cov}(V_{hTj} V_{iTk}) = 0 \quad \begin{cases} j, k = 1, ..., s \\ \quad j \neq k \end{cases} \qquad (5.31)$$

for any machine h in $[M_j]$ and any machine i in $[M_k]$, where h and i may
be the same machine. (5.31) is satisfied if (5.28) holds not only for two
machines operating in any two hours in one year but also for any two
machines (or the same machine), one in T_j and one in T_k, for any pair of
operating hours in these two years.

On the basis of these assumptions the necessary conditions for estimating (5.20) and (5.21) by ordinary least squares from a combination of the
time series and cross-section data in each of the vintage fuel cells would
be met, such that the estimates of the parameters of (5.20) and (5.21) and
hence of models A and B are best linear unbiassed. But there is no *a
priori* reason for (5.30a) to hold. Further, it is unlikely that condition
(5.19) holds for different machines in any one year (see footnote 9) and

even more so for the same machine operating in different years. Hence it is unlikely that the conditions for general homoscedasticity prevail so that there is probably a loss of efficiency if (5.20) and (5.21) are estimated by ordinary least squares.

We see then, that the implication of using T-period data to estimate a t-period process involves questions of aggregation and the nature of the disturbance terms in both a cross section of observations on a set of plants in a single year, and in these cross sections for different years. The T-period variables necessary to estimate the parameters of the t-period ex-post production function are derived as a result of the aggregation procedure, and we have shown how they may be obtained from actual data.[10] Thus the problems of dynamic aggregation and the derivation of individual machine data from plant data have now been solved.

Finally, we may comment upon the economic sense of models A and B. The form of either model A or B allows for uniformly increasing or decreasing fuel input per unit of output according as α is negative or positive respectively. It was felt that the input of fuel would decrease as capacity was approached and this in fact showed up in the results which are elaborated in section 5.3. An alternative hypothesis is that the ex-post production function is U-shaped implying that the minimum fuel input per unit of output occurs at less than 100 per cent of capacity output, but a functional form of this nature does not have the desirable aggregation properties that have been discussed here. The questions of whether the function is convex or concave, and what effects changes in the scale of machines have on fuel input per unit of output, when output is held constant, are answered by considering the values of the parameters which were determined by fitting the models to the sample data. A discussion of the results of the estimation now follows.

5.3.   The estimated ex-post production functions

The T-period equations (5.20) and (5.21), derived from models A and B respectively, were fitted to the sample data. Because of the relatively small number of plants of the mixed fuel type (except for the 1945–50 vintage)

---

[10]   In chapter 3.

TABLE 5.3

Regression results for the T-period model derived from model A.

t-period model: $a_{it} = \alpha \left(\dfrac{X_{it}}{X_{iK}}\right)^{-1} + \beta X_{iK} + \gamma + v_{it}$

estimated T-period model: $a_{iTj} = \alpha \left(\dfrac{X_{iTj}}{T_{1ij}X_{iK}}\right)^{-1} + \beta X_{iK} + \gamma + V_{iTj}$

Vintage	$\hat{\alpha}$	$\hat{\beta}$	$\hat{\gamma}$	$\bar{R}^2$
(i) Coal and mixed plants				
1920–24	73 599.4***	− 173.5	20 600.8	0.8651
	(29 291.0)	(15.0)	(409.0)	
1925–29	− 63 412.4**	− 121.1	20 745.0	0.5594
	(27 466.3)	(9.1)	(691.5)	
1930–39	75 894.8	− 90.8	15 273.9	0.6175
	(15 134.6)	(7.9)	(373.9)	
1940–44	272 264.9***	− 114.7	15 417.8	0.5555
	(120 333.5)	(16.0)	(1 866.6)	
1945–50	223 514.8	− 40.9	11 371.5	0.7851
	(15 981.6)	(3.1)	(289.9)	
1951–53	64 738.0**	− 37.3	12 622.9	0.7524
	(43 639.3)	(5.9)	(799.8)	
(ii) Non-coal plants				
1920–24	–	–	–	–
1925–29	188 993.6	− 365.0	20 624.5	0.6870
	(58 746.2)	(34.2)	(1 089.3)	
1930–39	227 768.0	− 282.9	16 582.1	0.6827
	(29 559.7)	(36.6)	(803.2)	
1940–44	66 602.8	− 18.8	12 389.4	0.6868
	(7 375.4)	(6.0)	(160.0)	
1945–50	57 243.5**	− 68.1	14 142 3	0.5183
	(40 852.9)	(11.0)	(619.8)	
1951–53	224 911.9	− 47.4	11 584.7	0.6055
	(53 511.1)	(8.6)	(932.0)	

Note: **, ***, imply not significantly different from zero at the 5 and 1 per cent levels respectively.

TABLE 5.4

Regression results for the T-period model derived from model B.

t-period model: $a_{it} = \alpha \left(\dfrac{X_{it}}{X_{iK}}\right)^{-1} + \beta\,(X_{iK})^{-1} + \gamma + v_{it}$

estimated T-period model: $a_{iTj} = \alpha \left(\dfrac{X_{iTj}}{T_{1ij}X_{iK}}\right)^{-1} + \beta\,(X_{iK})^{-1} + \gamma + V_{iTj}$

Vintage	$\hat{\alpha}$	$\hat{\beta}$	$\hat{\gamma}$	$\bar{R}^2$
(i) Coal and mixed plants				
1920–24	43 786.6**	118 397.0	11 064.0	0.7812
	(36 560.8)	(14 216.4)	(1 309.9)	
1925–29	38 501.6**	40 437.6	12 497.7	0.8202
	(16 225.2)	(1 593.1)	(314.5)	
1930–39	10 114.4*	46 192.3	11 358.5	0.5761
	(18 990.1)	(4 457.0)	(272.2)	
1940–44	115 759.5***	32 614.1	10 437.9	0.9090
	(55 233.3)	(1 505.5)	(673.4)	
1945–50	61 588.3	27 604.4	10 529.1	0.8268
	(20 119.2)	(1 763.5)	(221.8)	
1951–53	142 670.2	16 943.7	8 604.0	0.7770
	(38 078.2)	(2 484.1)	(489.1)	
(ii) Non-coal plants				
1920–24	–	–	–	–
1925–29	169 358.8	56 747.2	10 480.0	0.8594
	(39 425.7)	(3 139.3)	(656.6)	
1930–39	218 293.3	23 035.1	9 858.8	0.9223
	(14 005.4)	(999.7)	(269.8)	
1940–44	56 136.6	8 273.3**	11 633.7	0.6254
	(6 912.5)	(5 969.3)	(288.0)	
1945–50	95 040.2	25 439.7	10 048.1	0.9122
	(17 635.5)	(1 358.1)	(283.0)	
1951–53	118 983.8	29 810.8	9 698.2	0.8789
	(31 589.8)	(2 245.3)	(432.6)	

Note: *, **, *** imply not significantly different from zero at the 10, 5 and 1 per cent levels respectively.

these were combined with coal plants in each vintage strata. Also, because there were only five plants in the 1930–34 vintage, these were combined with the 1935–39 vintage plants. The estimated ex-post production
functions are shown in tables 5.3 and 5.4.[11]

On the whole it would seem that the estimated equation (5.21) was a
better fit to the data than equation (5.20). This was certainly true for non-
coal plants although the difference is less noticeable for coal and mixed
plants. Thus for the purpose of the following analyses model B is accepted
as the ex-post production function.

For each of the estimated equations (5.21) the estimates of α, β and γ
are all positive. Consider now the properties of the ex-post production
function for a particular machine of size X_{iK}. We have from model B,
equation (5.18), that

$$\frac{\partial a_{it}}{\partial \left(\frac{X_{it}}{X_{iK}}\right)}\Bigg|_{X_{iK}\text{ constant}} = X_{iK}\frac{\partial a_{it}}{\partial X_{it}}\bigg|_{X_{iK}\text{ constant}} = -\alpha\left(\frac{X_{it}}{X_{iK}}\right)^{-2} \tag{5.32}$$

and also that

$$\frac{\partial^2 a_{it}}{\partial \left(\frac{X_{it}}{X_{iK}}\right)^2}\Bigg|_{X_{iK}\text{ constant}} = X_{iK}\frac{\partial^2 a_{it}}{\partial X_{it}^2}\bigg|_{X_{iK}\text{ constant}} = 2\alpha\frac{X_{iK}^2}{X_{it}^3}. \tag{5.33}$$

Since $\hat{\alpha} > 0$ the ex-post production function for the ith machine of size
X_{iK} is of negative slope throughout the range of capacity utilisation and
convex to the origin as in figure 5.1. The set of ex-post production functions for machines of different sizes may now be considered. For any two
machines of capacity X_{iK} and X_{jK} and such that $X_{iK} > X_{jK}$ we have from
model B that[12]

$$a_{it} - a_{jt} = \beta\left(\frac{1}{X_{iK}} - \frac{1}{X_{jK}}\right) < 0 \tag{5.34}$$

---

[11] Certain additional results are given in the appendix to this chapter. Also see
Appendix D, p. 181, where the analysis of this chapter is presented for the subsample
of plants which have only one machine. This avoids certain problems relating to the
measurement of the degree of capacity utilisation which we have employed.

[12] In this analysis and those which follow, the error terms are omitted. Thus this discussion refers to the expected values of fuel input per unit of output.

at any common level of capacity utilisation since $\hat{\beta} > 0$. Hence regardless of the degreeof capacity utilisation, if we compare any two machines, the larger will use less fuel per unit of output and this saving in fuel will be constant over the range of capacity utilisation.

Suppose that

$$X_{iK} = X_{jK} + 1 \tag{5.35}$$

then from (5.34) we have that

$$a_{it} - a_{jt} = \frac{-\beta}{(X_{jK} + 1)\, X_{jK}}. \tag{5.36}$$

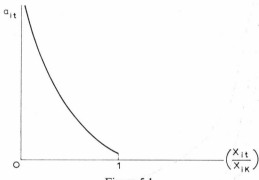

Figure 5.1.

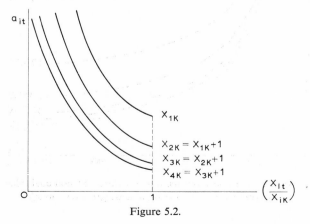

Figure 5.2.

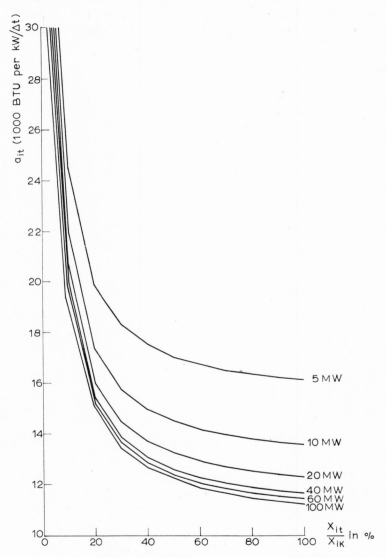

Figure 5.3.   Model B. Ex-post production functions for non-coal plants: vintage 1945–50. X_{it}/X_{iK} on horizontal axis. (Δt is one hour.)

Hence the larger is X_{jK} the smaller is the reduction in fuel input per unit of output when a machine one unit larger is considered. The set of ex-post production functions is then a family of curves of negative slope such that any two specified curves are the same vertical distance apart; but this distance varies for different pairs. If we compare a set of machines such that the increment in size is the same for any ordered pair in the set,[13] the vertical distance between the curves decreases as the size of machine increases and the X_{it}/X_{iK} axis is approached. A schematic representation of these ex-post production functions is shown in figure 5.2 and an actual estimated set of functions is shown in figure 5.3 (approximated by linear segments). These ex-post production functions are asymptotic to the a_{it} axis, but the range of capacity utilisation near zero is generally not observed.

Thus far we have considered model B as plotted with the degree of capacity utilisation X_{it}/X_{iK}, on the horizontal axis. It is useful to consider the function plotted with output X_{it} on the horizontal axis. The unit time period Δt is taken to be one hour, hence X_{it} is measured in kilowatthours and for the ith machine we have that

$$\max X_{it} = 1000\, X_{iK} \qquad (5.37)$$

where X_{iK} is measured in megawatthours, i.e. thousand kilowatthours.

From equation (5.32) we see that the absolute value of the slope of the production function plotted on X_{it} as the horizontal axis is less than when the degree of capacity utilisation is measured on the horizontal axis (see figure 5.4), but the two ways of presenting the ex-post production function lead to curves of the same general shape. However, when we consider the set of ex-post production functions of model B for machines of different sizes the diagrammatic form of the family of functions cannot be as simply represented as when the degree of capacity utilisation X_{it}/X_{iK} is plotted on the horizontal axis.

We may define the term "dominance" as implying that a production function lies uniformly below another so that the input of fuel per unit of output or of capacity utilisation is less. Thus when the ex-post production function is plotted on X_{it}/X_{iK} as the horizontal axis there is dom-

---

[13] Ordered by size of machine.

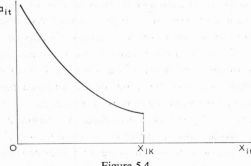

Figure 5.4.

inance over the full range of capacity utilisation, with a machine of capacity X_{iK} dominating all machines j where $X_{jK} < X_{iK}$. However, this is not the case when X_{it} is plotted on the horizontal axis.

Consider any two machines of sizes X_{iK} and X_{jK} where $X_{iK} > X_{jK}$. Then we have from model B equation (5.18) that

$$a_{it} - a_{jt} \gtreqqless 0 \qquad (5.38)$$

as [14]

$$\frac{\alpha}{100X_t}(X_{iK} - X_{jK}) + \beta\left(\frac{1}{X_{iK}} - \frac{1}{X_{jK}}\right) \gtreqqless 0 \qquad (5.39)$$

at any common level of output, $X_{it} = X_{jt} = X_t$. Then (5.39) implies that

$$X_t \lesseqqgtr \frac{X_{iK}X_{jK}}{100\left(\dfrac{\beta}{\alpha}\right)} \qquad \text{for } \beta > 0 \qquad (5.40)$$

Thus, in general, production functions for the ith and jth machine will cross when the equality in (5.40) holds and X_{it} is plotted on the horizontal axis. The question then arises whether this intersection is relevant, that is whether it occurs over the range of operation of a machine given by (5.37).

---

[14] The number 100 is introduced since in the estimation procedure X_{it}/X_{iK} is measured in per cent.

If the intersection of two production functions is not relevant, then the value of X_t for the equality in (5.40) must be greater than the size of the smaller machine. Thus for there to be no relevant intersection we must have that

$$\frac{X_{iK}X_{jK}}{100\left(\dfrac{\beta}{\alpha}\right)} > X_{jK} \tag{5.41}$$

therefore

$$X_{iK} > 100\left(\frac{\beta}{\alpha}\right), \qquad \text{for}\ \frac{\beta}{\alpha} > 0. \tag{5.42}$$

Thus when we compare the production functions of two machines of sizes X_{iK} and X_{jK} where $X_{iK} > X_{jK}$, the smaller will dominate up to an output given by the equality in (5.40) and for greater outputs the larger will dominate, provided that X_{iK} does not satisfy (5.42). If, however, X_{iK} satisfies (5.42) then the smaller machine will dominate over the full range of output of the smaller machine. These two cases are represented in figure 5.5a and 5.5b respectively.

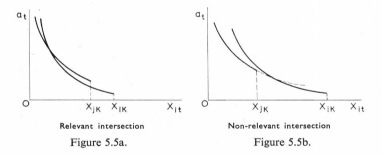

Relevant intersection   Non-relevant intersection

Figure 5.5a.   Figure 5.5b.

It would seem then that if we consider the set of ex-post production functions for any vintage fuel-type cell with output plotted on the horizontal axis, then certain of the production functions will have relevant intersections. The region of relevant intersections will depend on the value of $\hat{\beta}/\hat{\alpha}$ and these are given in table 5.5. These results show that the range of relevant intersections varies widely in the vintage fuel-type cells. For example, the machines of 1920–24 vintage which burn coal or mixed

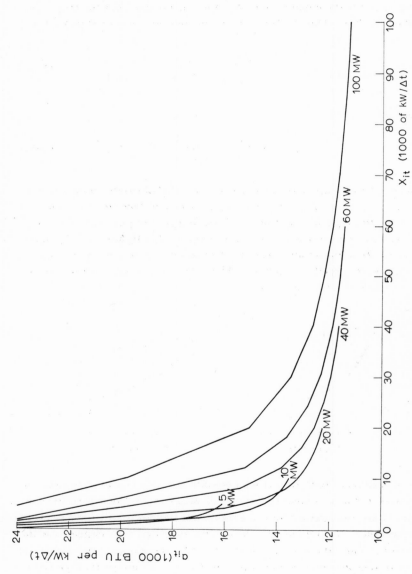

Figure 5.6.   Model B. Ex-post production functions for non-coal plants: vintage 1945–50. X_{it} on horizontal axis. (Δt is one hour.)

fuel have production functions with relevant intersections up to sizes of
270 megawatts, while for 1951–53 coal and mixed machines this is true
for machines of size 12 megawatts and less. As an illustration, figure 5.6
presents a set of ex-post production functions for the 1945–50 non-coal
machines (approximated by linear segments) where relevant intersections
occur between machines of less than or equal to 27 megawatts.

TABLE 5.5

Values of $\hat{\beta}/\hat{\alpha}$ for model B.

Vintage	Coal and mixed plants	Non-coal plants
1920–24	2.70	–
1925–29	1.05	0.34
1930–39	4.57	0.11
1940–44	0.28	0.15
1945–50	0.45	0.27
1951–53	0.12	0.25

Finally, when model B is drawn with X_{it} measured on the horizontal
axis, the locus of points of (X_{iK}, a_{iK}) where a_{iK} is the input of fuel per unit
of output at capacity, must be a curve of negative slope and convex to the
origin. This follows by considering the set of ex-post production functions
plotted on the X_{it}/X_{iK} axis at the level of full capacity operation as in
figure 5.3, or by considering the exact form of the locus of full capacity
points which is given by

$$a_{iK} = \frac{\alpha}{100} + \frac{\beta}{X_{iK}} + \gamma \qquad (5.43)$$

where

$$\frac{da_{iK}}{dX_{iK}} = \frac{-\beta}{(X_{iK})^2} < 0 \qquad (5.44)$$

and

$$\frac{d^2 a_{iK}}{dX_{iK}^2} = \frac{2\beta}{(X_{iK})^3} > 0. \qquad (5.45)$$

5.4. Cost functions derived from the ex-post production function of model B

If fuel is regarded as the only variable input used by a machine[15] and the price of fuel is assumed constant for the machine operator then variable cost curves and the marginal cost curve may be derived for each machine of a given size, vintage and fuel type. For simplicity take the price per BTU of fuel to be unity. Then for machine i we have that,

$$\text{AVC}_i = a_{it} \tag{5.46}$$

$$\text{TVC}_i = X_{it}a_{it} = \alpha X_{iK} + X_{it}\left(\frac{\beta}{X_{iK}} + \gamma\right) \tag{5.47}$$

and

$$\text{MC}_i = \frac{\partial \text{TVC}_i}{\partial X_{it}} = \frac{\beta}{X_{iK}} + \gamma. \tag{5.48}$$

Thus the particular form of ex-post production function fitted to the data implies a linear total variable cost and constant marginal cost curve shown in figure 5.7. The fact that the TVC curve does not go through the origin is due to the form of the ex-post production function. In chapter 3 (p. 37) the total fuel input function was shown to be double valued at zero

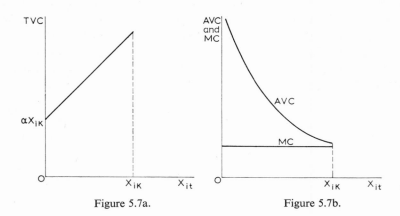

Figure 5.7a.   Figure 5.7b.

---

[15] See chapter 6, where labour input is considered.

output due to fuel input when the machine operates hot and not connected to load, which would imply that the TVC function is also double valued at zero output. However, the vertical axis intercept in figure 5.7a cannot be taken as an estimate of fuel cost per hour when the machine operates hot and not connected to load[16] for it is solely a result of the form of the estimated production function.

We may surmise that the linear TVC function estimated is an approximation to the true TVC function which is concave to the horizontal axis

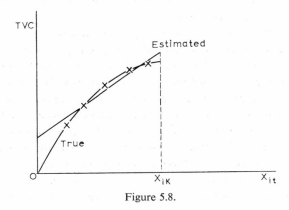

Figure 5.8.

as in figure 5.8. Thus over the greater part of the output range of a machine the estimated cost function may be taken to be a reasonable approximation to the true cost function.

If the true total variable cost function is convex to the cost axis as in figure 5.8, then generally the relevant level of operation of such a machine will be at full capacity (see the appendix to chapter 3) and we may concentrate on the level of full capacity operation of machines in the discussion of economies of scale and technological change which follows.

---

[16] From (5.47):

$$\frac{\text{TVC at capacity}}{\text{TVC at zero output}} = \frac{\beta + (\alpha + \gamma)\, X_{iK}}{\alpha X_{iK}} = 1 + \frac{\gamma}{\alpha} + \frac{\beta}{\alpha X_{iK}}$$

which is very different from the 100:1 value of this ratio implied in actual operation (see footnote 16, p. 44).

5.5.   Scale economies and technological change

The stratification technique first employed by Komiya[17] and used in this study, enables the effects of changes in scale and technological change on the production process to be distinguished. Scale effects are reflected in shifts of the ex-post production function for machines of different sizes but of the same vintage and fuel type while embodied technological change is identified by observing shifts of the ex-post production function for machines of the same size and fuel type but of different vintage. First we shall consider scale economies.

For any machine of a specific vintage, size and fuel type, the ex-post production function falls over the full range of capacity. Thus there are intra-capacity economies[18] in the use of fuel, for if output increases in more than proportion to fuel input this implies that the average input of fuel per unit of output decreases as full capacity is approached.

If machines in any vintage fuel-type cell are compared at capacity output we have seen that the fuel input per unit of output decreases the larger is the machine, but this fuel saving diminishes as machines of successively larger scale are compared.[19] Thus scale economies exist over the full range of the sample. Table 5.6 presents the effects of economies of scale in each vintage for machines of both fuel types. We see that the relative strength of scale economies varies over the different vintages. For example in fuel category (i), coal and mixed machines, a 50 MW machine used only 39.4 per cent of fuel per unit of output at capacity, when compared with a 5 MW machine in the 1920–24 vintage, but this figure was only 77.3 per cent in the 1951–53 vintage. It would seem then by comparing columns that the degree of scale economies diminished over time for coal and mixed machines, while for non-coal machines this was not evident.[20] The

---

[17] See p. 61.

[18] Defined p. 24.

[19] See p. 111.

[20] Note that the same result may be obtained by considering equation (5.44) above which gives the slope of the locus of full capacity points when model B is plotted on X_{it} as the horizontal axis. This slope varies as β and hence for coal and mixed plants where $\hat{\beta}$ diminishes uniformly over time (apart from the 1930–39 vintage), the absolute value of this slope falls for given X_{iK} and thus the degree of scale economies diminishes over time.

The coal and mixed category was separated for the 1935–39 and 1945–50 vintages

figures represented in table 5.6 effectively show movements "along a production function" where this is to be understood as a comparison between ex-post production functions of machines of the same vintage at the level of full capacity operation. Now what of movements of the production function due to embodied technological change which are reflected in shifts of the family of ex-post production functions between vintages.

First, suppose that we wish to compare two machines of the same size X_K and fuel type but of vintages i and j. Then we have that

$$a_{Ki} \gtreqless a_{Kj}$$

as

$$\frac{\left(\dfrac{\hat{\alpha}_i}{100} + \hat{\beta}_i\right) - \left(\dfrac{\hat{\alpha}_j}{100} + \hat{\beta}_j\right)}{\hat{\beta}_j} + \frac{\hat{\beta}_i}{\hat{\beta}_j}\frac{1}{X_K} \gtreqless \frac{1}{X_K} \quad \text{for } \hat{\alpha}_j, \hat{\beta}_j > 0 \quad (5.49)$$

where a_{Ki} is fuel input per unit of output at capacity of a machine of vintage i and the subscripts refer to the particular vintage group to which model B is fitted. Then from (5.49) it is possible to derive the conditions on X_K such that machines of later vintages save on fuel input at capacity. Table 5.7 shows that the effects of technological change have been somewhat uneven when two adjacent vintages are compared but over the range of the sample the effect of technological change has been to save on fuel input. The specific effects of technological change are shown in table 5.8 for machines up to the size of 100 megawatts, at capacity levels of operation.

The effects of technological change in shifting the production function are shown by reading across any row in table 5.8. Thus over the period of the sample technological change has acted so as to reduce fuel requirements for machines of the same size in either of the two fuel-type cat-

---

and the same analysis was carried out using the regression results in the appendix to this chapter. It was found that the degree of scale economies was somewhat stronger for mixed machines than for coal machines in both vintages and the degree of scale economies diminished for both coal and mixed machines of the 1945–50 vintage compared with the 1935–39 vintage. However, the regression equations used here were less satisfactory than those in table 5.4. But these results suggest that the fact that the degree of scale economies seemed to diminish over time is not a specious effect due to the grouping of coal and mixed machines.

TABLE 5.6

Economies of scale.

Size			Vintage			
X_K	1920–24	1925–29	1930–39	1940–44	1945–50	1951–53
(i) Coal and mixed machines						
5	35 181	20 970	20 695	18 118	16 665	13 419
	(=100)	(=100)	(=100)	(=100)	(=100)	(=100)
10	66.3	80.7	77.7	82.0	83.4	87.4
20	49.5	71.1	66.5	73.0	75.2	81.1
30	43.9	67.9	62.8	70.0	72.4	79.0
40	41.1	66.3	60.9	68.5	71.0	77.9
50	39.4	65.3	59.8	67.6	70.2	77.3
60	38.3	64.6	59.1	67.0	69.6	76.9
80	36.9	63.8	58.1	66.2	68.9	76.3
100	36.1	63.4	57.6	65.8	68.5	76.0
(ii) Non-coal machines						
5		23 523	16 649	13 850	16 086	16 850
		(=100)	(=100)	(=100)	(=100)	(=100)
10		75.9	86.2	94.0	84.2	82.3
20		63.8	79.2	91.0	76.3	73.5
30		59.8	76.9	90.0	73.6	70.5
40		57.8	75.8	89.5	72.3	69.0
50		56.6	75.1	89.2	71.5	68.2
60		55.8	74.6	89.0	71.0	67.6
80		54.8	74.1	88.8	70.3	66.8
100		54.2	73.7	88.7	70.0	66.4

Note: X_K is size of machine in megawatts. The table measured a_K which is input of fuel per kilowatthour at capacity. Thus

$$a_K = \left(\frac{\hat{\alpha}}{100} + \hat{\gamma}\right) + \frac{\hat{\beta}}{X_K} \text{ derived from model B.}$$

The row of 5 MW measures a_K in BTU's; the remaining rows measure a_K as an index with the fuel input at capacity for a 5 MW machine set equal to 100 in each vintage column.

TABLE 5.7

Shifts in the ex-post production function due to technological change

(i) Coal and mixed machines

a_K 20–24 $\gtreqless$ a_K 25–29   for $X_K \leqq 56.5$
a_K 25–29 $>$ a_K 30–39   for all X_K
a_K 30–39 $\gtreqless$ a_K 40–44   for $X_K \leqq 99.9$
a_K 40–44 $>$ a_K 45–50   for all X_K
a_K 45–50 $>$ a_K 51–53   for all X_K
a_K 20–24 $>$ a_K 51–53   for all X_K

(ii) Non-coal machines

a_K 25–29 $>$ a_K 30–39   for all X_K
a_K 30–39 $>$ a_K 40–44   for all X_K
a_K 40–44 $\gtreqless$ a_K 45–50   for $X_K \gtreqless 14.3$
a_K 45–50 $\gtreqless$ a_K 51–53   for $X_K \gtreqless 39.6$
a_K 25–29 $>$ a_K 51–53   for all X_K

egories. It would seem that newly embodied technology has been relatively more effective in reducing fuel requirements for coal and mixed machines than for non-coal machines over the period 1925 to 1953. Also the larger is the machine the smaller has been the effect (in relative terms) of technological change in reducing fuel requirements.

5.6. A comparison of coal and mixed plants and non-coal plants

A comparison between the ex-post production function of machines in the two fuel-type categories is not strictly valid because there is no exact distinction made here between the nature of the fuel actually burned in mixed plants and non-coal plants. But if the ex-post production functions estimated for coal and mixed plants are taken as representative of coal plants then a distinction may be made. If (5.49) is used where the subscripts i and j refer to coal and mixed plants and non-coal plants respectively the results in table 5.9 are derived where a_{Kc} and a_{Kn} are fuel input per unit of output at capacity for coal and mixed machines and non-coal machines respectively. There is no uniform pattern over the different vin-

TABLE 5.8

Technological change

Size (X_K)	Vintage					
	1920–24 (=100)	1925–29	1930–39	1940–44	1945–50	1951–53

(i) Coal and mixed machines

Size (X_K)	1920–24 (=100)	1925–29	1930–39	1940–44	1945–50	1951–53
5	35 181	59.6	58.8	51.5	47.4	38.1	(63.9)
10	23 342	72.5	68.9	63.6	59.6	50.2	(69.2)
20	17 422	85.6	79.0	75.9	71.9	62.4	(72.9)
30	15 456	92.1	84.1	82.1	78.1	68.6	(74.5)
40	14 462	96.1	87.2	85.8	81.8	72.3	(75.2)
50	13 870	98.7	89.3	88.3	84.3	74.8	(75.8)
60	13 475	100.6	90.7	90.1	86.1	76.5	(76.0)
80	12 982	103.1	92.7	92.5	88.5	78.9	(76.5)
100	12 686	104.7	94.0	94.0	90.0	80.4	(76.8)

(ii) Non-coal machines

Size (X_K)		(=100)				
5	–	23 523	70.8	58.9	68.4	71.6
10	–	17 848	80.4	73.0	75.9	77.7
20	–	15 011	87.9	84.0	81.7	82.5
30	–	14 065	91.1	88.7	84.2	84.5
40	–	13 592	92.8	91.2	85.6	85.6
50	–	13 309	93.9	92.9	86.5	86.3
60	–	13 119	94.7	94.0	87.1	86.8
80	–	12 883	95.7	95.5	87.8	87.4
100	–	12 741	96.3	96.4	88.3	87.8

Note: Derived from the estimates of model B. The second column shows input of fuel per unit of output at capacity, a_K, in BTU's (this is the third column for non-coal machines, for there were no 1920–24 non-coal machines in the sample). The remaining columns show a_K as an index with the 1920–24 value (or 1925–29 value in part (ii)) set equal to 100 in each row. In addition, the last bracketed column in part (i) is this index for 1951–53 with 1925–29 taken as 100. This is done in order to be able to compare both fuel types. X_K is measured in megawatts.

·TABLE 5.9

A comparison between coal and
mixed machines and non-coal machines

Vintage

1925–29	$a_{Kc} \gtreqless a_{Kn}$	for $X_K \gtreqless 23.0$
1930–39	$a_{Kc} \gtreqless a_{Kn}$	for $X_K \lesseqgtr 39.8$
1940–44	$a_{Kc} \gtreqless a_{Kn}$	for $X_K \lesseqgtr 40.6$
1945–50	$a_{Kc} > a_{Kn}$	for all X_K
1951–53	$a_{Kc} < a_{Kn}$	for all X_K

TABLE 5.10

Range of the sample
(machine sizes in megawatts).

Vintage	Coal and mixed	Non-coal
1920–24	15–50	–
1925–29	4–68	6–35
1930–39	7.5–80	2–31.25
1940–44	2.5–100	15–65.0
1945–50	3.75–152	5–110.0
1951–53	5–100	5–80.3

tages but clearly there is a distinction in the ex-post production functions
for machines of the two fuel categories.[21]

5.7.   Conclusions on technological change and economies of scale

We have seen that both scale economies and technological change have
had significant effects on the production process in steam-electric power

---

[21] It should be noted that these results, although of some significance in themselves, are
not important for the investment decision of the steam-electric firm, unless they are
combined with data of costs for the various fuels.

generation. The techniques employed here have enabled these effects to be distinguished quantitatively for readily identifiable units of capital. In addition, new technology has enabled larger machines to be installed and table 5.10 shows the range of the sample in each of the vintage fuel-type cells. These figures do not adequately represent the actual changes of scale of machines in the industry due to the necessity of choosing the sample of plants to include only those with identical machines. The first 100 MW unit and 160 MW unit were placed in service in 1928, and in 1958 the first 300 MW unit was installed. By 1960 units of 1000 MW were in use.[22] Thus an important feature of technological change has been the introduction of larger machines. A shortcoming of the analysis of the production process of steam-electric power presented in this study is that the size range of machines considered is somewhat smaller than that actually in place. But this has been necessitated by the techniques employed here and the availability of the data.

Finally it should be noted that the discussion of economies of scale and technological change has dealt with plants operating at full capacity, but the form of the ex-post production function estimated enables the effects of scale and technological change to be measured at any level of capacity operation of machines.

Appendix

Certain additional estimates of the parameters of models A and B are given here. In table 5.4 the estimated T-period equation of model B gives a poor fit to the data for the 1930–39 coal and mixed plants with $\hat{\alpha}$ not significantly different from zero at the 10 per cent level. The breakdown of plants into coal, non-coal and mixed for the period 1935–39 provides somewhat better estimates of model B for non-coal plants and mixed plants than those presented in table 5.4 for 1930–39 coal plants, and these could be used in further analysis.

---

[22] For data on this see the *FPC Report: 1962–63*, p. v.

MODEL A

Vintage	$\hat{\alpha}$	$\hat{\beta}$	$\hat{\gamma}$	$\bar{R}^2$
(i) Coal plants				
1935–39	39 178.7***	− 162.8	17 376.8	0.6392
	(17 187.5)	(16.0)	(552.3)	
1945–50	259 936.7	− 46.2	11 142.4	0.8626
	(19 864.2)	(3.2)	(338.2)	
(ii) Non-coal plants				
1935–39	252 856.1	− 185.1	14 530.2	0.7171
	(26 349.2)	(31.6)	(697.6)	
(iii) Mixed plants				
1935–39	55 120.1**	− 79 2	14 946.9	0.8582
	(33 646.2)	(5.8)	(393.1)	
1945–50	204 173.3	− 28.9	11 099.1	0.7020
	(25 821.4)	(6.5)	(515.9)	

MODEL B

Vintage	$\hat{\alpha}$	$\hat{\beta}$	$\hat{\gamma}$	$\bar{R}^2$
(i) Coal plants				
1935–39	21 393.3*	40 825.2	11 599.5	0.4943
	(22 910.7)	(5 866.9)	(370.8)	
1945–50	96 591 2	25 087.1	10 181.6	0.8290
	(30 380.1)	(2 025.6)	(339.5)	
(ii) Non-coal plants				
1935–39	212 288.0	26 454.7	9 596.4	0.8833
	(17 278.7)	(1 940.8)	(303.2)	
(iii) Mixed plants				
1935–39	55 120.1**	63 351.3	10 195.6	0.8582
	(33 646.2)	(4 632.1)	(495.1)	
1945–50	− 2 518.8*	36 385.2	11 001.4	0.8449
	(32 889.2)	(4 138.4)	(325.7)	

Notes: *, **, *** imply not significantly different from zero at the 10, 5 and 1 per cent levels, respectively.

CHAPTER 6

CAPITAL AND LABOUR IN STEAM-ELECTRIC POWER GENERATION

In this chapter we investigate certain of the effects of changes in scale and technology on the input of capital and labour in the steam-electric power industry. The effect of differences in machine-mix on the capital and labour requirements for plants is explicitly considered. Unfortunately the quality of the data is less satisfactory than that used for the estimation of the ex-post production function in chapter 5, thus the results presented here, especially for labour input, leave much to be desired. The sample of plants and years of observation used to estimate the ex-post production function was also employed in this analysis.

6.1. Capital input

The choice of the sample used to estimate the ex-post production function limited the investigation of capital cost to that for coal plants and mixed plants in the 1945–50 vintage and to non-coal plants in the 1951–53 vintage. The objective was to determine the effects of machine-mix on capital cost of plants when plants comprised of machines of the same size and vintage are compared. It was postulated that the capital cost per machine in a plant is a function of the size of machine and the number of machines in a plant. Thus

$$\frac{C_T}{N} = f(N, X_K) \qquad (6.1)$$

where C_T is the total capital cost of a plant, which is the sum of the costs of land and land rights, structures and improvements and equipment; N is the number of machines in the plant and X_K is the size of each machine. The function f will vary for plants which have machines of different vintage and fuel type.

What may be expected regarding the shape of equation (6.1)? As the number of machines of the same size and vintage increases in a plant it is likely that there will be initially a reduction in capital costs per machine due to the use of ancillary equipment over more than one machine, and saving in the capital cost of land and structures.[1] In addition the fact that turbines are made to order implies that discounts are likely to be given by the manufacturer when more than one unit is ordered. This would also tend to reduce the capital cost per unit *ceteris paribus*. However, it is unlikely that the capital cost per machine would fall continuously as the number of units in the plant increases, for beyond a certain size of plant further ancillary equipment, land and structures would have to be purchased which would tend to raise the capital cost per machine in the plant.

Thus it is likely that if we compare plants which are composed of machines of the same size, vintage and fuel type but which vary in terms of the number of machines in a plant, capital cost per machine will fall for $0 \leq N \leq N^*$ and rise for $N > N^*$, for some number N^*.[2] We may say then, that there are economies of capital cost for these plants when they have N^* or fewer machines and diseconomies of capital cost when they have more than N^* machines.

Before proceeding with an exact determination of such economies of capital cost two points must be mentioned. Firstly, the capital cost we have been discussing includes land and land rights. It is likely that the price of land and land rights varies geographically so that this element of capital cost is not uniform for the plants in our sample. The same criticism applies to the cost of structures,[3] but may be weaker than when applied to land. In order to allow for this criticism the function (6.2)

---

[1] A plant comprised of two machines presumably will not have double the structures and land cost of a plant with one machine of the same size, vintage and fuel type.

[2] Other hypotheses are possible. E.g., capital cost per machine may first fall and then as N increases tend to level off. But this leveling-off process may not be smooth. Also, see the appendix to this chapter.

[3] We are assuming here that at any point of time the cost of a machine of a specific size, vintage and fuel type is the same country-wide, apart from transport costs and perhaps special installation charges which are not considered. If this is not the case then a geographical price index of equipment would also be required.

was also considered where C_E is the total equipment cost of a plant.

$$\frac{C_E}{N} = f(N, X_K).$$ (6.2)

Secondly the prices per unit of land and land rights, structures and equipment are unlikely to be constant over time. Ideally then, we should like to have geographical and temporal price indices of the cost per unit of land and land rights, structures and equipment in order to deflate the capital cost data given in the FPC Reports. Geographical price indices do not seem to be available and although temporal price indices of the cost of capital exist they are not adequate for our analysis.[4] We need in principle the temporal price index of land and land rights, structures and equipment for plants comprised of machines of the same size, vintage and fuel type which vary only in the number of machines in a plant, but the existing indices do not reflect this. In addition the FPC Reports give no indication of the year in which the capital cost of a plant was actually paid, thus if adequate indices were available an assumption would have to be made regarding the actual time of payment. Lastly, the vintage fuel-type cells considered in this analysis are of relatively short duration, 1945–50 and 1950–53, and in the first period most of the plants began operation during the period 1948–50. Hence the costs per unit of land and land rights, structures and equipment in the two vintage groups may be assumed to relate to approximately the same period. Thus in the analysis which follows the total capital cost and equipment cost of plants were not deflated by either a geographical or a temporal price index.

The functional forms of (6.1) and (6.2) were taken to be identical in the estimation procedure and specified as

$$\frac{C_T}{N} \quad \text{or} \quad \frac{C_E}{N} = \alpha_1 N + \alpha_2 N^2 + \alpha_3 N^3 + \beta X_K.$$ (6.3)

---

[4] For example: Y. BARZEL, The Production Function and Technical Change in the Steam Power Industry, *The Journal of Political Economy*, LXXII, April 1964, p. 148, and W. IULO, *Electric Utilities – Costs and Performance*, Washington State University Press, 1961, p. 47.

Variation in the cubic $g(N)$ given by (6.4) will determine the extent of economies and diseconomies of capital cost.

$$g(N) = \alpha_1 N + \alpha_2 N^2 + \alpha_3 N^3 \qquad (6.4)$$

The results of fitting equation (6.3) to the vintage fuel cells of the sample which had an adequate number of plants are given in table 6.1 where C_T and C_E are measured in thousands of dollars and X_K in megawatts.

In all these estimated equations $\hat{\beta}$ is positive, thus, as is expected, the total capital and equipment cost per machine increases with the size of

TABLE 6.1

Regression equations for capital input.

Dependent variable	$\hat{\alpha}_1$	$\hat{\alpha}_2$	$\hat{\alpha}_3$	$\hat{\beta}$	$\bar{R}^2$
(a) Coal plants, vintage 1945–50					
$\dfrac{C_T}{N}$	5 372.9	− 3 437.7	462.7	137.8	0.8780
	(1 026.1)	(764.6)	(116.8)	(11.1)	
$\dfrac{C_E}{N}$	2 975.3	− 1 931.7	259.8	102.8	0.9305
	(584.9)	(435.9)	(66.6)	(6.3)	
(b) Mixed plants, vintage 1945–50					
$\dfrac{C_T}{N}$	9 422.1	− 7 322.8	1 516.5	90.7	0.9219
	(2 033.2)	(1 500.0)	(290.8)	(21.1)	
$\dfrac{C_E}{N}$	5 622.9	− 4 428.0	929.9	74.0	0.9473
	(1 199.3)	(884.8)	(171.5)	(12.4)	
(c) Non-coal plants, vintage 1951–53					
$\dfrac{C_T}{N}$	5 835.2***	− 4 715.2***	987.7**	84.8	0.5684
	(2 298.0)	(2 140.5)	(503.2)	(17.4)	
$\dfrac{C_E}{N}$	4 461.0***	− 3 745.4***	783.9**	66.5	0.6012
	(1 693.6)	(1 577.5)	(370.9)	(12.8)	

Note: **, ***, imply not significantly different from zero at the 5 and 1 per cent levels, respectively.

machine. The estimated equations for C_E/N give a somewhat better fit than those for C_T/N in the three vintage fuel-type categories of table 6.1. This is to be expected due to the lack of uniformity in land and construction costs which are excluded in the estimation of equipment cost per machine.

An analysis of the function $g(N)$ for the three vintage fuel-type cells in table 6.1 is given in table 6.2. These results show that for group (a), coal plants in the 1945–50 vintage, both total capital cost per machine and equipment cost per machine fall for plants of from one to three machines

TABLE 6.2

Analysis of the function $g(N)$.

	$\dfrac{dg(N)}{dN} > 0$	Local maximum	$\dfrac{dg(N)}{dN} < 0$	Local minimum
(a) Coal plants, vintage 1945–50 (range of N in sample, from 1 to 5)				
$\dfrac{C_T}{N}$	$-\infty \le N < 0.97$ $\quad N > 3.98$	$N = 0.97$	$0\,97 < N < 3.98$	$N = 3.98$
$\dfrac{C_E}{N}$	$-\infty \le N < 0.96$ $\quad N > 3.87$	$N = 0.96$	$0\,96 < N < 3.87$	$N = 3.87$
(b) Mixed plants, vintage 1945–50 (range of N in sample, from 1 to 4)				
$\dfrac{C_T}{N}$	$-\infty \le N < 0.89$ $\quad N > 2.33$	$N = 0.89$	$0.89 < N < 2.33$	$N = 2.33$
$\dfrac{C_E}{N}$	$-\infty \le N < 0.88$ $\quad N > 2.30$	$N = 0.88$	$0.88 < N < 2.30$	$N = 2.30$
(c) Non-coal plants, vintage 1951–53 (range of N in sample, from 1 to 3)				
$\dfrac{C_T}{N}$	$-\infty \le N < 0.84$ $\quad N > 2.34$	$N = 0.84$	$0.84 < N < 2.34$	$N = 2.34$
$\dfrac{C_E}{N}$	$-\infty \le N < 0.79$ $\quad N > 2.34$	$N = 0.79$	$0.85 < N < 2.34$	$N = 2.34$

and then rise for larger N. For group (b), mixed plants of 1945–50 vintage, and group (c), non-coal plants of the 1951–53 vintage, total capital cost per machine and equipment cost per machine are smaller for plants of two machines compared with one machine and then begin to increase for larger N. Hence economies of capital cost are present in the three vintage fuel-type categories analysed.

Finally, we may compare the capital costs of coal plants and mixed plants in the 1945–50 vintage strata where subscripts "a" refer to coal plants and "b" to mixed plants in table 6.3. These results show that for

TABLE 6.3

Comparison of capital costs of coal plants and mixed plants of the 1945–50 vintage

(i) $\quad \left(\dfrac{C_T}{N}\right)_a \gtreqless \left(\dfrac{C_T}{N}\right)_b$

for $X_K \gtreqless 26.5,$ when $N = 1$
for $X_K \gtreqless 23.5,$ when $N = 2$
for $X_K \gtreqless 125.4,$ when $N = 3$

(ii) $\quad \left(\dfrac{C_E}{N}\right)_a \gtreqless \left(\dfrac{C_T}{N}\right)_b$

for $X_K \gtreqless 28.5,$ when $N = 1$
for $X_K \gtreqless 23.3,$ when $N = 2$
for $X_K \gtreqless 123.9,$ when $N = 3$

plants of one or two machines both total capital cost per machine and equipment cost per machine is greater for coal plants when the size of machine is greater than from 23.3 to 28.5 megawatts. However, when N is three or larger, the number on the right-hand side of the condition on X_K in table 6.3 increases, which implies that both total capital cost per machine and equipment cost per machine is lower for coal plants than for mixed plants as the number of units in the plant increases above three.[5]

---

[5] The range of both coal and mixed plants in the sample from the 1945–50 vintage is from 4 MW to 150 MW.

6.2. Labour input

The analysis of labour input had three objectives: to determine how machine-mix and the size of machine affected labour requirements, to estimate the effects of technological change on labour requirements, and lastly to determine whether the degree of capacity utilisation affected the labour requirements of plants.

Only plants in the sample used for estimating the ex-post production function for fuel were considered; thus we consider only those plants which had machines of the same size and vintage. We postulated a labour input function of the form

$$L = h(N, X_K, u) \qquad (6.3)$$

where L is labour input, N is the number of machines in the plant, X_K is the size of unit and u is a capacity utilisation measure. The function h will vary for plants of different vintage fuel-type. Unfortunately the only measure for L given in the FPC reports is "average number of employees" in a year. This is a poor measure of labour input for it excludes differences in the length of the working day or week over time and other conditions that may change as a result of variations in labour contracts over time. Further, in any year these conditions may vary geographically. But there are no other data readily available so that the unadjusted "average number of employees" published in the FPC Reports was used as a measure of labour input.

Three different capacity measures u were tried, t_1 the number of hours in the year when the plant is operated hot and connected to load, $t_1 + t_2$ the number of hours in the year when the plant is operated hot connected and unconnected, and PF* the adjusted plant factor.[6] It was found that PF* was the best capacity variable for explaining labour input.

The final estimated model was of the form

$$L = \alpha + \beta_1 N + \gamma X_K + \delta \text{PF}^*. \qquad (6.4)$$

Additional terms in N^2 and N^3 were tried, and also (6.4) was forced

---

[6] See chapter 3 for a discussion of these measures.

TABLE 6.4

Regression equations for labour input

Vintage	$\hat{\alpha}$	$\hat{\beta}_1$	$\hat{\gamma}$	$\hat{\delta}$	$\bar{R}^2$
(i) Coal and mixed plants					
1925–29	− 83.443	29.788	1.797	0.857	0.7067
	(14.321)	(2.424)	(0.159)	(0.182)	
1930–39	− 46.137	26.524	1.000	0.458	0.9086
	(4.405)	(1.299)	(0.055)	(0.048)	
1940–44	− 131.027	53.265	0.656	1.125	0.8505
	(22.299)	(3.732)	(0.173)	(0.242)	
1945–50	− 38.538	20.644	0.837	0.330	0.8462
	(7.127)	(1.841)	(0.054)	(0.081)	
(ii) Non-coal plants					
1925–29	− 10.099*	13.150	1.331	0.029*	0.7598
	(5.150)	(1.180)	(0.127)	(0.067)	
1930–39	− 3.314*	7.781***	1.570	− 0.014*	0.6701
	(5.189)	(3.906)	(0.146)	(0.046)	
1940–44	21.860*	13.583	0.961	− 0.310***	0.7443
	(16.336)	(2.937)	(0.186)	(0.115)	
1945–50	− 1.040*	8.511	0.870	0.001*	0.7969
	(10.530)	(1.933)	(0.104)	(0.111)	
1951–53	− 23.168***	15.939***	0.301	0.304***	0.5533
	(10.728)	(5.615)	(0.084)	(0.117)	

Note: *, ***, imply not significantly different from zero at the 10 and 1 per cent levels respectively.

through the origin, but the results were poorer in each case. The model (6.4) was fitted to the vintage fuel-type cells of table 5.2, where the data were adequate and the results are given in table 6.4.

From these results it is seen that the model (6.4) gives a reasonable fit to the data for coal and mixed plants but was poor in explaining labour requirements for non-coal plants. Thus the following analysis will be limited to coal and mixed plants.

For such plants in each of the four vintage strata, $\hat{\delta}$, the coefficient of

PF* (measured in per cent) is small but significantly different from zero beyond the 1 per cent level of significance. This implies that labour requirements for coal are significantly affected by the degree of capacity utilisation.[7] In table 6.5 the labour requirements for plants consisting of from one to three units are given when each plant operates at full capacity (when PF* is 100 percent). These figures are derived from the estimation of equation (6.4) in table 6.4 part (i).

The scale effects on labour input are shown by reading down the columns for each of the vintage strata considered. It is seen that for a constant number of machines N, the labour input increases proportionately less than the increase in the size of machine in each of the vintage groups. Also, if we compare plants of the same size and vintage but composed of different numbers of machines the input of labour increases less than proportionately to N. Thus there are economies in labour use in each vintage for plants of a given machine size but varying N, and for plants of the same N but varying machine size.

The effects of technological change may be seen by reading across rows in table 6.5. However, it must be remembered that changes in employment conditions over time are compounded with the effects of technological change. This may be evident in the 1940–44 vintage for $N = 3$ when compared with the 1930–39 vintage, where if we may assume that technological change led to a reduction in labour requirements for plants of the same size and number of machines, the increase in labour requirements is presumably due to special employment conditions during wartime and different employment conditions in existence after 1945. Over the period of the sample, however, a significant reduction in labour requirements had taken place which in part may be interpreted as the result of technological change.

These results are less than satisfactory, however, for the reasons already mentioned and especially for machines of size 5 to 40 megawatts, give a relatively poor fit to the data.

---

[7] However, a study of the data would suggest that labour input is relatively unaffected by the degree of capacity utilisation over a significantly wide range. Thus this result may be somewhat spurious due more to the poor quality of the data and changes in working conditions over time than to a "true" capacity effect.

TABLE 6.5

*Labour requirements for coal and mixed plants
(average number of employees in a year).*

Size X_K	Vintage			
	1925–29	1930–39	1940–44	1945–50
$N=1$				
5	41.1	31.1	38.0	19.3
10	50.1	36.1	41.3	23.5
20	68.0	46.2	47.9	31.9
30	86.0	56.2	54.4	40.2
40	104.0	66.2	61.0	48.6
50	121.9	76.2	67.5	57.0
60	139.9	86.2	74.1	65.3
80	175.9	106.2	87.2	82.1
100	211.8	126.2	99.8	98.8
$N=2$				
5	70.9	57.7	91.3	40.0
10	79.8	62.7	94.6	44.1
20	97.8	72.7	101.1	52.5
30	115.8	82.7	107.7	60.9
40	133.8	92.7	114.3	69.3
50	151.7	102.7	120.8	77.6
60	169.7	112.7	127.4	86.0
80	205.7	132.7	140.5	102.7
100	241.6	152.7	153.0	119.5
$N=3$				
5	100.6	84.2	144.6	60.6
10	109.6	89.2	147.9	64.8
20	127.6	99.2	154.4	73.2
30	145.6	109.2	161.0	81.5
40	163.6	119.2	167 5	89.9
50	181.5	129.2	174.1	98.3
60	199.5	139.2	180.6	106.6
80	235.4	159.2	193.7	123.4
100	271.4	179.2	206.3	140.1

6.3. Summary

In this chapter certain of the effects of changes in machine-mix and technology on the inputs of labour and capital have been investigated. It has been shown that there are economies of labour input and capital cost as the size of machines and the number of machines in a plant varies. Further, technological change has been labour saving. The degree of capacity utilisation also seems to be a significant variable in explaining labour input, but for small changes in capacity the effect is small. However, the analyses of labour input are far from satisfactory due to the quality of the data. Finally it must be remembered that the analysis of capital and labour input is only applicable to plants composed of machines of the same size, vintage and fuel type.

Appendix

Critique of the capital-input function[8]

The capital-input function specified in the chapter is of the form

$$\frac{C_T}{N} \quad \text{or} \quad \frac{C_E}{N} = \alpha_1 N + \alpha_2 N^2 + \alpha_3 N^3 + \beta X_K, \qquad (6.5)$$

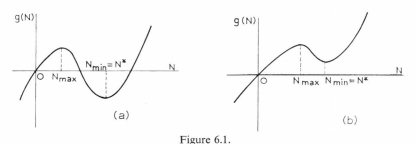

Figure 6.1.

---

[8] This appendix is the result of comments on the capital cost functions of chapter 6 by Professor Willem Somermeyer of the Econometric Institute of the Netherlands School of Economics.

where it is assumed that there are likely to be economies of capital cost resulting from the inclusion of more than one unit in the plant. These economies are expressed by the cubic function of N

$$g(N) = \alpha_1 N + \alpha_2 N^2 + \alpha_3 N^3 . \qquad (6.6)$$

It was stated that there are likely to be economies of capital cost for values of N less than or equal to some value $N = N^*$, and then diseconomies for $N > N^*$. The implications of this assumption are shown in figures 6.1a and b[9] where $N_{max} \leq 1$.

No *a priori* restrictions were imposed on the estimating procedure to ensure that such results would be realised. The necessary *a priori* restrictions on the parameters of $g(N)$ would be
for form (a): $\alpha_1 > 0, \alpha_2 < 0, \alpha_3 > 0, \alpha_2^2 - 3\alpha_1\alpha_3 > 0,$
and for form (b): $\alpha_1 > 0, \alpha_3 > 0, \alpha_2^2 - 4\alpha_1\alpha_3 < 0.$
In addition, $N_{max} \leq 1$ must hold.

In fact, the results obtained from fitting (6.5) to data resulted in a function $g(N)$ of the form (a) in figure 6.1 for both cost functions of coal plants, vintage 1945–50, and for equipment cost for non-coal plants, vin-

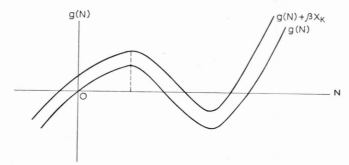

Figure 6.2.

---

[9] Two other cubic forms are also consistent with the assumption, viz.,

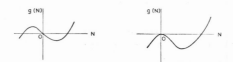

tage 1951–53. In the other three cases $g(N)$ conformed to (b) of figure 6.1. If the form of $g(N)$ is that of figure 6.1a, it is possible that for N sufficiently large and X_K sufficiently small total capital costs would be negative – an absurd result. This is shown in figure 6.2 with $\beta > 0$.

As an example, the calculation of C_T/N for a coal plant, vintage 1945–50 composed of four machines each of size 25 MW, yields $-\$453,800$! It is possible to impose additional restrictions to ensure that this result does not occur, but the constrained estimating procedure would be difficult.

As an alternative, Professor Somermeyer has proposed a capital input function of the form

$$C_E \quad \text{or} \quad C_T = c_0 (\alpha + N)(\delta + X_K) \tag{6.7}$$

where c_0, α and δ are constants. He and Teekens, a research assistant of his, have developed iterative methods of estimating this non-linear function. This work is to be published at a later date.

We concur with these criticisms of Somermeyer, and also with his point that if $\alpha_3 > 0$ (as is the case in the fitted equations) capital cost per unit increases indefinitely with N. It should be noted that in Somermeyer's suggested function capital cost per unit tends to zero as the number of units increases indefinitely. However, we believe that given the range of N and X_K in the sample, and the fact that negative capital costs cannot occur in three of the six estimated equations, the function (6.5) provides a reasonable approximation to capital cost.[10] But any more detailed analysis would require a different specification perhaps along the lines suggested by Somermeyer.

---

[10] At least for small N or large X_K.

CHAPTER 7

EXAMPLES OF COST CALCULATIONS FOR THE STEAM-ELECTRIC GENERATING PLANT

In the previous chapters we have estimated functions for fuel, capital and labour input in the steam-electric plant. From the ex-post production functions of chapter 5 we may calculate the cost of fuel input for each machine in the plant, given the price of fuel. From the labour input functions of chapter 6 total labour cost for the plant may be calculated given the price of labour. And from the capital-input functions of chapter 6 we may estimate the total capital cost directly. Hence with this information we are able to determine the total operating cost and capital cost of a plant of any machine-mix, which may operate its machines at varying degrees of capacity.[1]

We now present some calculations for illustrative purposes only. For any realistic investment decision an electric utility will have to take into account other factors in addition to those that have been discussed, e.g., the necessary reserve capacity to meet the problem of outage, and the relationship between total capacity and peak load. We shall not consider these problems here. What follows is simply the total fixed and variable cost calculations for a steam-electric generating plant which would be required to produce a specified output in a year, and which may have different machine-mixes. These cost calculations will be an important part of any realistic investment decision.

We shall confine our calculations to coal plants of vintage 1945–50. The relevant input functions are as follows:[2]

---

[1] This is not quite correct for there will be some operating (or variable) costs other than for fuel and labour. But since fuel and labour costs account for 90 per cent or more of total operating costs our calculations will very closely approximate total cost.

[2] The ex-post production function (7.1) and the capital-input function (7.3) refer to coal plants, vintage 1945–50. The labour-input function (7.2) refers to coal and mixed plants, vintage 1945–50. The sources of (7.1), (7.2) and (7.3) are pp. 127, 136 and 132, respectively.

$$a_{it} = 96\ 591.2 \left(\frac{X_{it}}{X_{iK}}\right)^{-1} + 25\ 087.1\ (X_{iK})^{-1} + 10\ 181.6, \qquad (7.1)$$

$$L = -38.538 + 20.644N + 0.837X_{iK} + 0.330PF^*, \qquad (7.2)$$

$$\frac{C_T}{N} = 5\ 372.9N - 3\ 437.7N^2 + 462.7N^3 + 137.8X_{iK} \qquad (7.3)$$

where

a_{it} is the input of fuel per kilowatthour per turbine measured in BTU'S,

$\left(\dfrac{X_{it}}{X_{iK}}\right)$ is the degree of capacity utilisation of the turbine in an hour measured in per cent,

X_{iK} is the size of the turbine measured in megawatts (thousand kilowatts),

L is the average number of employees in the plant in a year,

N is the number of turbines in the plant,

PF^* is the degree of capacity utilisation of the plant measured in per cent,

C_T is the total capital cost of the plant measured in $1000.

We shall assume that two plants are to be built, one to produce 100 MW and the other 200 MW for each hour in a year. Also we restrict the choice of machine-mixes to:

	N	X_{iK}
for the 100 MW plant	1	150
	1	100
	2	60
	2	50
for the 200 MW plant	1	200
	2	100
	3	70
	4	50

When total plant capacity equals desired output, all units will be assumed to operate at 100 per cent of capacity. When plant capacity is greater than desired output, as many machines as possible operate at full

TABLE 7.1

Examples of cost calculations for steam-electric generating plants

Plant output per year	N	X_{IK}	A	Ap_F	L	Lp_L	$Lp_L + Ap_F$	C_T
8.76 × 10⁶ kWh	1	150	15.502	3.876	129.7	0.441	4.316	23.068
8.76 × 10⁶ kWh	1	100	9.985	2.496	98.8	0.336	2.832	16.178
8.76 × 10⁶ kWh	2	60	10.301	2.575	80.5	0.274	2.849	17.929
8.76 × 10⁶ kWh	2	50	10.205	2.551	77.6	0.264	2.815	15.173
17.52 × 10⁶ kWh	1	200	19.750	4.938	182.5	0.621	5.558	29.958
17.52 × 10⁶ kWh	2	100	19.970	4.992	119.4	0.406	5.399	28.953
17.52 × 10⁶ kWh	3	70	21.265	5.316	113.4	0.386	5.702	21.955
17.52 × 10⁶ kWh	4	50	20.409	5.102	129.1	0.439	5.541	22.989

Apart from the symbols defined on p. 144.
A is annual fuel input measured in 10^{12} BTU's,
Ap_F is annual fuel cost measured in 10^6 dollars,
Lp_L is annual labour cost measured in 10^6 dollars,
$Ap_F + Lp_L$ is annual operating cost measured in 10^6 dollars.

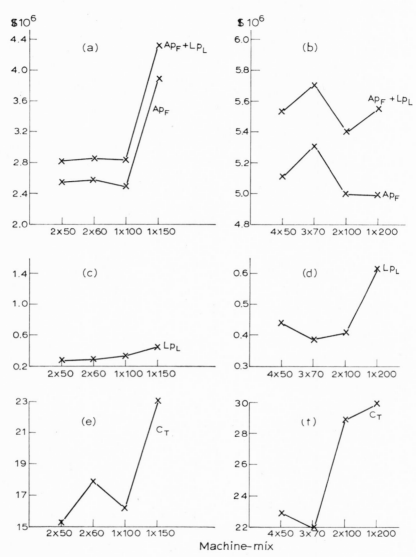

Figure 7.1.   Plant costs. (a, c, e): Plant with output 8.76×10^6 kWh; (b, d, f): Plant with output 17.52×10^6 kWh.

TABLE 7.2

Present values of total costs

Plant output (10^6 kWh)	N	X_{iK}	PVC (10^6)
8.76	1	150	56.061
8.76	1	100	37.429
8.76	2	60	39.852
8.76	2	50	36.892
17.52	1	200	72.011
17.52	2	100	71.456
17.52	3	70	67.214
17.52	4	50	66.427

capacity and the remaining output is produced on the other machine. For example, the plant which must produce 200 MW and which is composed of 3 machines each of size 70 MW has two turbines operating at 100 per cent of capacity and a third operating at 85.6 per cent of capacity in each hour of the year.

The results of these cost calculations are shown in table 7.1 and figure 7.1, where the annual labour cost per employee is taken to be $3400,[3] and the fuel cost 25c per million BTU's.

The optimal choice of plant may now be determined. We shall assume that all capital costs must be met when the plant is built, that there is no depreciation and that the plant scrap value is zero. In each of the two cases the present value of gross revenue will be the same for a plant of any machine mix, hence that plant will be chosen which has the smallest present value of total costs.

---

[3] The annual labour cost figure is an approximation to the average annual earnings plus supplements for employees in electric light and power for the years 1946–50. See *Historical Statistics of the United States*, U.S. Bureau of the Census, Washington, D.C., 1960, pp. 94 and 96.

The fuel cost estimate is taken from S. LING, *Economies of Scale in the Steam-Electric Power Generating Industry*, Amsterdam: North Holland Publishing Company, 1964, p. 36.

The present value of total costs is given by[4]

$$\mathrm{PVC} = [Ap_F + Lp_L]\frac{1}{r}\left(1 - \frac{1}{(1+r)^t}\right) + C_T \qquad (7.4)$$

where r is the discount rate and t is the time horizon used in the investment calculation.[5] The results of these calculations are shown in table 7.2 for $r = 10\%$ and $t = 20$ years. Thus the optimal plant to produce 100 MW continuous, should be composed of two turbines each of size 50 MW, and to produce 200 MW continuous, a plant with four turbines each of size 50 MW should be chosen.

It should be noted that the optimal choice of plant will depend on the values of r and t and the implied assumption of a fixed output in every year over the time horizon.

---

[4] For simplicity, p_F and p_L are assumed constant over the time horizon.

[5] Note that

$$\sum_{s=1}^{t} \frac{1}{(1+r)^s} = \frac{1}{r}\left(1 - \frac{1}{(1+r)^t}\right).$$

CHAPTER 8

CONCLUSIONS

This study has been a theoretical and empirical analysis of the effects of technological change and changes in scale on the production process in the multi-unit plant. The example chosen was that of the steam-electric plant, due to the availability of data on a plant-by-plant basis for this industry in the United States. The level of analysis has been in micro-economic terms with the machine, the turbine generator and its ancillary equipment, viewed as the basic unit of capital. The problem of measuring capital input has been avoided by characterising the machine by means of a measure of size and by identifying the vintage and fuel type. Plants, however, are often composed of more than one machine, and the problems of machine-mix of plants have been explicitly considered throughout the analysis. Further, the operation of machines at various degrees of capacity utilisation has also been considered.

We have seen that the theoretical analysis of the production process in the multi-unit plant and the application of these ideas to the steam-electric plant, has involved modifications of conventional production theory. In addition, certain interesting econometric problems have been raised. In particular, we have discussed the estimation of cost problems in a dynamic setting, and the derivation of empirical correlates of desired theoretical variables has involved consideration of a special form of the aggregation problem. Thus, this detailed investigation of the production process in steam-electric power generation has taken into account many factors which are peculiar to the industry and which have been omitted in attempts to apply more conventional theory to an analysis of the production process.[1] This strengthens our feeling that although analyses in macro-terms are both relevant and useful, they may hide more information than they show, and also, that analyses in micro-terms which

---

[1] See chapter 5.

attempt to apply conventional theory without any modifications for the particular characteristics of the micro-units being considered, may be in serious error.

The analysis of the production process in steam-electric power generation has enabled the effects of changes in scale and technology to be separated and quantified. Technological change has resulted in a reduction in labour and fuel requirements for machines of the same size and fuel type and in each vintage group considered, there are economies of scale with respect to both fuel and labour. Further, when plants as a whole are considered the choice of machine-mix will substantially affect capital and labour requirements even if we consider only plants of a given overall capacity size which are composed of machines of the same vintage.

It should be stressed again that the form of technological change we have considered is actual rather than virtual technological change, i.e., we consider the introduction of new technology into the plant rather than the addition of blueprints to the ex-ante production function. It is entirely possible then, that a machine first put into operation in 1953, say, was available to the industry in 1945, but given factor prices, the form of the optimal investment decision of the plant operator did not dictate the introduction of the machine until 1953. Thus, shifts in the ex-post production function as presented in this study are due to virtual technological change which may be compounded with changes in relative factor prices and the nature of the investment decision of the plant operator. Hence, we measure actual or ex-post technological change.

Knowledge of the production process is useful for its own sake, but more important, it determines many of the relevant factors which the plant operator must take into account in formulating his investment decision and outlines the range of choice of capital and other inputs (the substitution possibilities) available to him. The investment decision in steam-electric power generation has not been considered in detail in this book. We have seen that the long-run cost curves for the plant may be derived (Appendix to chapter 2), and that operating and capital costs may be calculated (chapter 7). However, the relevant investment decision is complicated, not least by the fact that because of the longevity of capital in this industry, optimisation over a substantial period of time is required. Faced by uncertain demands and a life of capital of perhaps 20 years, a correct optimisation procedure involves that choice of plant which maximises the present value of expected profits, or in the case of a set of exogenous demands, that plant should be built which meets these demands at minimum cost. Further consideration of the problems involved in the investment decision would take us beyond the bounds of the present book.

To conclude then, this study was prompted by an interest in applying certain theoretical concepts of production theory to a concrete situation. We believe that economic theory should be, in many instances, a guide to empirical analysis and not a straight jacket into which reality should be squeezed. It is left to the reader to judge how far we have succeeded in this endeavour.

APPENDIX A

Data used for the estimation of the ex-post production function and the labour input function

Column (1): Identification, e.g. (i) 34135, (ii) 1405316.

The number on the far right refers to the vintage of machines in the plant. The code is as follows:

Number	Vintage
1	1920–24
2	1925–29
3	1930–34
4	1935–39
5	1940–44
6	1945–50
7	1951–53

Then, reading from right to left the next number indicates the fuel type of machine(s) in the plant. The code is as follows:

Number	Fuel type
1	Coal
2	Non-coal
3	Mixed

The next two numbers represent the year of observation in the period 1938 to 1953. Finally the remaining numbers indicate the identity of the plant.[1]

Thus example (i) refers to observations in 1941 on plant number 3, a mixed plant of 1940–44 vintage, and example (ii) refers to observations on plant number 140, in 1953, a coal plant of 1945–50 vintage.

Column (2): Machine size, X_K. Measured in megawatts (thousand kilowatts). Source, FPC Reports.

---

[1] See Appendix C for plant identification.

Column (3): Capacity utilisation measure, PF*. Measured in per cent. For the calculation of PF* see chapter 3.

Column (4): Fuel input per unit of output, *B*. *B* is measured in BTU's per kilowatthour of net generation. Source, FPC Reports.

Column (5): Number of machines in the plant, *N*. Source, FPC Reports.

Column (6): Average number of employees in a year, *L*. Source, FPC Reports.

Notes
(a) In a very few cases PF* could not be calculated because the breakdown of hours was not given, thus PF, the published plant factor, was used as a proxy.
(b) In a few cases *B* was not published and so it was calculated from data of physical fuel input using BTU content of an adjacent year.
(c) Plants are reported with different numbers of machines when the added machines were of the same size and vintage as those initially installed.
(d) When a plant began working during a year, the labour-input figure was not used for that year, but PF* was calculated when the breakdown of hours was given. Similarly in the year when machines were added to a plant neither PF* nor a figure of labour input was used and these years did not appear in the sample.
(e) The vintage year of a machine refers to the initial year of commercial operation of the plant. Thus a machine added in 1940 to a plant that began operation in 1938, which was of the same size and type as existing machines in the plant, is classified as a 1938 machine.
(f) In a few cases plants had additional small house-service units. These were ignored in the analysis.
(g) The symbol – implies that data were not recorded or not used for the reasons mentioned in note (d).
(h) The symbol Δ implies that the plant is in its first year of operation.
(i) The symbol * implies that the plant operates hot but not connected to load for certain hours in the year.
(j) The symbol NR implies that either no data were given on hours so that the plant factor was used for PF*, or that hours operated hot but not connected are not reported, but PF* could be calculated.

(1)	(2)	(3)	(4)	(5)	(6)
14422	6.0	73.0	20444	3	–
14522	6.0	59.4	21651	3	27
14622	6.0	56.7	22426	3	38
14722	6.0	51.9	24346	3	41
14822	6.0	64.3	22195	3	50
14922	6.0	60.7	21426	3	46
15022	6.0	62.0	21911	3	35
15122	6.0	67.1	21484	3	34
15222	6.0	68.2	22020	3	33
15322	6.0	63.9	22478	3	33
23812	4.0	59.1	22600	1	12
23912	4.0	46.6*	22334	1	12
24012	4.0	47.6	24453	1	–
24112	4.0	51.7	24265	1	–
24212	4.0	56.5	23969	1	10
24312	4.0	68.6	23015	1	10
24412	4.0	73.4	22698	1	17
24512	4.0	73.5	23266	1	17
24612	4.0	75.8	24058	1	10
24712	4.0	87.1	23052	1	11
24812	4.0	89.1*	22859	1	10
24912	4.0	82.6	22583	1	10
25012	4.0	79.8	22213	1	11
33822	6.5	51.0	24850	1	12
33922	6.5	54.7	22280	1	16
34022	6.5	52.1	22100	1	16
34122	6.5	56.8	23150	1	16
34222	6.5	59.6	22863	1	17
34322	6.5	68.0	22970	1	16
34422	6.5	69.0	22970	1	13
34522	6.5	75.5	21760	1	14
34622	6.5	83.6	21450	1	15
34722	6.5	80.1	22430	1	16
34822	6.5	71.9	23060	1	14
34922	6.5	58.6	23800	1	16
35022	6.5	70.2	19965	1	16
35122	6.5	67.9	20169	1	16
35222	6.5	59.3	21348	1	17
35322	6.5	52.8	22144	1	17
43812	10.0	30.3*	16349	2	39
43912	10.0	36.5*	16290	2	39
44012	10.0	36.7*	15608	2	34
44112	10.0	31.4*	15955	2	37

(1)	(2)	(3)	(4)	(5)	(6)
44212	10.0	32.2*	15788	2	36
44312	10.0	34.8*	15754	2	35
44412	10.0	32.2*	15919	2	35
44512	10.0	31.4*	16215	2	35
44612	10.0	39.7*	16064	2	37
44712	10.0	60.1*	16330	2	41
44812	10.0	68.6*	16289	2	41
44912	10.0	51.1*	16037	2	39
45012	10.0	39.1	16626	2	42
45112	10.0	36.2	16887	2	41
45212	10.0	30.3*	16739	2	40
53823	2.0	50.3*	24593	1	9
53923	2.0	54.9*	24379	1	–
54023	2.0	55.1*	23466	1	8
54123	2.0	51.7*	24862	1	8
54223	2.0	53.5*	25346	1	8
54323	2.0	56.0*	24153	1	8
54423	2.0	59.4*	23648	1	9
54523	2.0	58.1*	24464	1	9
54623	2.0	39.6*	28249	1	9
54723	2.0	32.9*	30199	1	9
64824	3.0	72.8	17060	1	6
64924	3.0	55.7	24680	1	6
65024	3.0	58.8	23700	1	–
65124	3.0	82.9	18600	1	–
65224	3.0	49.8	27900	1	–
65324	3.0	64.7	22638	1	–
74114	10.0	70.2*	16346	1	22
74214	10.0	56.9*	16465	1	22
74314	10.0	65.9*	16199	1	21
74414	10.0	63.8*	16034	1	19
74514	10.0	68.4*	16484	1	19
74614	10.0	75.4*	16299	1	22
74714	10.0	83.9*	16776	1	23
84615	2.5	42.7NR	26281	1	–
84715	2.5	55.9NR	28035	1	–
84815	2.5	72.1NR	27617	1	9
84915	2.5	66.5NR	24183	1	9
85015	2.5	80.9NR	22000	1	–
85115	2.5	88.0NR	22369	1	–
94826	5.0	107.3	15640	1	17
94926	5.0	103.1	15750	1	15
95026	5.0	98.6	15804	1	15

(1)	(2)	(3)	(4)	(5)	(6)
95126	5.0	112.0	16452	1	15
95226	5.0	106.7	16372	1	16
95326	5.0	90.2	16685	1	17
105036	3.8	22.2Δ	22611	2	–
105236	3.8	20.9	18703	2	12
113823	6.0	24.9*	21300	1	10
113923	6.0	27.1*	20576	1	10
114023	6.0	28.5	20715	1	10
114123	6.0	30.1	20475	1	10
114223	6.0	30.9	20207	1	11
114323	6.0	40.4	19685	1	11
114423	6.0	50.7	18708	1	11
114523	6.0	49.5	18781	1	10
114623	6.0	49.2	18601	1	10
114723	6.0	52.4	18677	1	–
114823	6.0	57.1	18579	1	10
123824	5.0	89.8	16611	1	6
123924	5.0	90.1	16116	1	6
124024	5.0	94.2*	15680	1	6
124124	5.0	94.6	16507	1	6
124224	5.0	99.4	16495	1	6
124324	5.0	27.2	21864	1	6
124424	5.0	26.8	21869	1	6
124524	5.0	26.7	21260	1	6
124624	5.0	43.5	19109	1	6
124724	5.0	51.5	20991	1	–
124824	5.0	84.4NR	17805	1	–
124924	5.0	85.9	17306	1	–
125024	5.0	36.9	20866	1	–
125124	5.0	24.9	23573	1	–
125224	5.0	18.9	26979	1	–
125324	5.0	17.2	27631	1	–
133924	10.0	52.3	14920	1	17
134024	10.0	61.4*	13990	1	–
134124	10.0	71.9	14000	1	17
134224	10.0	75.8	13700	1	15
134324	10.0	91.4*	13630	1	15
134424	10.0	94.6	13499	1	15
134524	10.0	92.7	13952	1	–
134624	10.0	102.0*	13598	1	–
134724	10.0	107.9*	14043	1	16
134824	10.0	106.7	13769	1	18
134924	10.0	100.0*	14255	1	18

(1)	(2)	(3)	(4)	(5)	(6)
135024	10.0	97.3	13616	1	17
135124	10.0	84.0*	14217	1	18
144114	7.5	17.5*	18114	2	18
144214	7.5	18.9	18434	2	24
144314	7.5	21.5	17382	2	21
144414	7.5	23.9	16425	2	18
144514	7.5	22.8	17382	2	18
144614	7.5	24.4	17575	2	18
144714	7.5	27.0	17096	2	17
144814	7.5	28.1	17024	2	18
144914	7.5	28.8	18226	2	20
154114	7.5	76.8*	15635	1	13
154214	7.5	68.0*	15890	1	19
154314	7.5	81.9*	15376	1	20
154414	7.5	63.0*	16071	1	20
154514	7.5	60.0*	15580	1	19
154614	7.5	61.0*	16210	1	19
154714	7.5	81.6*	15761	1	19
165016	4.0	32.1	18921	2	15
165116	4.0	34.4	18517	2	–
165216	4.0	35.4	18583	2	15
165316	4.0	37.1	18300	2	15
175117	5.0	81.8Δ	13367	1	–
175217	5.0	75.8	14181	1	12
195127	6.0	52.7Δ	15048	1	–
195227	6.0	51.5	14767	1	8
195327	6.0	36.2	18726	1	8
205227	6.0	56.2	16436	1	10
205327	6.0	64.3	16606	1	10
225016	7.5	68.7Δ*	16315	1	–
225116	7.5	56.9*	16753	1	18
225216	7.5	61.0*	16292	1	18
225316	7.5	81.4	15695	1	–
235036	7.5	57.4*	16455	1	18
235136	7.5	65.5*	15497	1	17
235236	7.5	61.7	16276	1	17
235336	7.5	72.6	15217	1	17
245226	6.0	64.7	15133	2	–
245326	6.0	38.5	15844	2	–
255016	6.0	57.2	16598	1	–
1315016	5.0	56.7	16553	2	33
1315116	5.0	55.1	16039	2	28
1315216	5.0	54.8	15713	2	27

(1)	(2)	(3)	(4)	(5)	(6)
1315316	5.0	53.2	15722	2	25
1324916	7.5	78.8	13360	1	36
1325016	7.5	82.1	15054	1	30
1325116	7.5	75.4	15004	1	28
1325216	7.5	74.6	14466	1	28
1325316	7.5	69.7*	15430	1	26
1505327	5.0	93.6	18228	1	5
263811	15.0	69.6	18233	2	47
263911	15.0	62.4*	18795	2	47
264011	15.0	80.2	17835	2	49
264111	15.0	91.0*	18305	2	46
264211	15.0	94.8	17599	2	50
264311	15.0	93.2*	18067	2	51
264411	15.0	85.1	18801	2	48
264511	15.0	70.3	18829	2	50
264611	15.0	32.1*	21164	2	48
264711	15.0	86.9	19266	2	48
264811	15.0	84.6*	19789	2	49
264911	15.0	51.3*	21350	2	50
265011	15.0	66.6*	22037	2	50
273812	12.5	25.7	20300	6	87
273912	12.5	28.6	20673	5	–
274012	12.5	31.6	20322	6	98
274112	12.5	39.4	20177	6	93
274212	12.5	42.1	20135	6	98
274312	12.5	44.1	19663	6	88
274412	12.5	44.6	19484	6	–
274512	12.5	44.7	19422	6	118
274612	12.5	42.5	19687	6	136
274712	12.5	47.9	19779	6	130
283822	12.5	28.2	17804	2	21
283922	12.5	45.4*	17502	2	24
284022	12.5	64.1	17543	2	26
284122	12.5	83.2	17720	2	29
284222	12.5	61.1*	17687	2	44
284322	12.5	78.0	17295	2	43
284422	12.5	85.2	17200	2	41
284522	12.5	68.5	17477	2	42
284622	12.5	59.8	17949	2	49
294124	15.0	73.4*	13154	1	23
294224	15.0	80.5*	12867	1	23
294324	15.0	92.9	13052	1	25
294424	15.0	87.5	13222	1	24

(1)	(2)	(3)	(4)	(5)	(6)
294524	15.0	95.6	13314	1	22
294624	15.0	102.0*	13315	1	24
294724	15.0	84.0*	12932	2	31
294824	15.0	96.5	13138	2	34
294924	15.0	88.3	12932	2	35
295024	15.0	81.9*	12689	2	35
295124	15.0	80.7	12786	2	35
295224	15.0	69.4	14732	2	35
295324	15.0	63.3	13702	2	34
304235	20.0	87.4*	13244	1	42
304335	20.0	68.1*	16596	1	40
304435	20.0	81.5*	15845	1	40
304535	20.0	64.6*	15621	1	38
304635	20.0	72.7*	15130	1	41
304735	20.0	55.0*	15693	2	45
304835	20.0	79.6*	15635	2	51
304935	20.0	77.1*	15143	2	51
305035	20.0	78.6*	13950	2	42
305135	20.0	65.7*	14486	2	42
314836	25.0	69.9	12440	1	35
315036	25.0	82.6	12382	1	48
315136	25.0	86.7*	12268	1	58
315236	25.0	90.1*	12069	1	58
315336	25.0	86.4	12316	1	49
325036	20.0	72.5*	14778	1	27
325136	20.0	77.0	15721	1	26
345016	11.5	74.2*	13970	2	26
345116	11.5	61.7*	14541	2	27
345216	11.5	70.9*	13612	2	27
345316	11.5	71.4*	13389	2	27
355236	11.5	67.6	13271	2	17
355336	11.5	67.5	13408	2	15
363922	15.0	54.8*	17762	1	15
364022	15.0	47.7*	18653	1	18
364222	15.0	57.9*	17810	1	27
364322	15.0	63.5	17878	1	27
364422	15.0	72.2	17630	1	23
364522	15.0	66.6	17753	1	21
364622	15.0	69.0	17771	1	26
364722	15.0	77.3	17913	1	27
364822	15.0	58.7	18516	1	26
364922	15.0	60.5*	18150	1	25
365022	15.0	73.7*	17949	1	27

(1)	(2)	(3)	(4)	(5)	(6)
365122	15.0	62.5*	18382	1	28
373822	20.0	76.5	14179	1	25
373922	20.0	78.7*	14165	1	29
374022	20.0	79.9	14483	1	29
374122	20.0	81.1	14556	1	31
374222	20.0	81.1	14174	1	38
374322	20.0	87.0	14337	1	38
374422	20.0	89.1	14145	1	36
374522	20.0	86.3	14310	1	29
374622	20.0	81.0	14443	1	29
374722	20.0	87.8	14152	1	30
374822	20.0	90.0	13474	1	28
374922	20.0	80.1*	14884	1	27
375022	20.0	80.1*	14884	1	27
383832	15.0	86.5	15375	1	39
383932	15.0	88.8	15142	1	40
384032	15.0	70.0	15137	1	39
384132	15.0	81.6	15299	1	37
384232	15.0	91.0	15045	1	32
384332	15.0	101.9	15133	1	33
384442	15.0	104.1	15277	1	33
384532	15.0	100.1	15356	1	34
384632	15.0	91.8	15955	1	40
384732	15.0	87.8	15049	1	–
393914	15.0	97.7*	15572	1	32
394014	15.0	106.7*	15066	1	36
394114	15.0	101.2*	15753	1	36
394214	15.0	103.8*	14983	1	37
394314	15.0	86.7*	16041	1	32
394414	15.0	84.2*	16668	1	30
394514	15.0	66.5*	21148	1	29
394614	15.0	69.7*	18990	1	36
394714	15.0	77.4*	16983	1	38
394814	15.0	88.2*	16614	1	38
394914	15.0	99.1*	16550	1	38
395014	15.0	48.8*	20447	1	18
395114	15.0	58.4*	17986	1	22
395214	15.0	48.2*	19365	1	22
395314	15.0	52.5*	19660	1	23
405116	15.0	69.5	14097	1	26
405216	15.0	75.9	14432	1	27
405316	15.0	76.6	14426	1	25
413924	23.0	73.2*	13440	1	34

(1)	(2)	(3)	(4)	(5)	(6)
414024	23.0	92.8*	13337	1	34
414124	23.0	104.0*	13224	1	41
414224	23.0	103.3*	13235	1	42
414324	23.0	103.4*	13452	1	36
414424	23.0	110.1*	13300	1	35
414524	23.0	110.2*	13383	1	36
414624	23.0	114.5*	13271	1	43
414724	23.0	109.7*	13361	1	41
424034	20.0	84.9*	14100	1	21
424134	20.0	91.2*	13800	1	–
424234	20.0	71.7*	14200	1	48
424334	20.0	78.0*	14215	1	48
424434	20.0	90.8*	13850	1	48
424534	20.0	76.9*	14435	1	48
424634	20.0	85.7*	14113	1	48
424734	20.0	90.7*	13964	1	56
424834	20.0	95.5*	13851	1	48
424934	20.0	90.6*	13208	1	–
425034	20.0	89.6*	13590	1	48
425134	20.0	90.6*	14086	1	40
425234	20.0	91.9*	13842	1	48
425334	20.0	90.4*	14748	1	48
434124	12.5	112.4*	14356	1	24
434224	12.5	104.4*	14164	1	24
434324	12.5	94.4*	15634	1	24
434424	12.5	90.1*	16564	1	24
434524	12.5	93.4*	16069	1	29
434624	12.5	94.2*	14715	1	25
434724	12.5	107.6*	14901	1	24
434924	12.5	112.2*	15083	1	24
435024	12.5	106.0*	14663	1	24
435124	12.5	96.3*	14566	1	26
435224	12.5	98.9*	14251	1	26
435324	12.5	89.6*	14728	1	26
444625	15.0	89.0	12183	1	31
444725	15.0	82.5	12437	1	34
444825	15.0	85.4	12485	1	32
444925	15.0	89.2	12245	1	32
454816	17.3	73.6	15079	1	17
454916	17.3	73.3	14573	1	17
455016	17.3	73.0	14082	1	17
455116	17.3	72.7*	14570	1	17
455216	17.3	69.6	13870	1	17

(1)	(2)	(3)	(4)	(5)	(6)
455316	17.3	68.5	13998	1	17
1334936	12.5	101.7*	13790	1	22
1335036	12.5	105.4*	13937	1	22
1335236	12.5	80.8*	13265	2	25
1335336	12.5	72.3	13224	2	25
1345036	12.5	80.2	14282	2	24
1355026	12.5	98.7	13700	4	54
1355126	12.5	94.2	13440	4	43
1355226	12.5	97.2	14030	4	42
1355326	12.5	101.9	13810	4	42
463811	25.0	48.0NR	18026	2	–
463911	25.0	50.0NR	17726	2	–
464011	25.0	46.0NR	18205	2	–
464111	25.0	47.0NR	17829	2	–
464211	25.0	43.0NR	17688	2	–
464311	25.0	45.0NR	17682	2	–
464411	25.0	51.0NR	17457	2	–
464511	25.0	55.0NR	17199	2	–
464611	25.0	48.0NR	17307	2	–
464711	25.0	57.0NR	17289	2	–
464811	25.0	55.0NR	16870	2	–
464911	25.0	52.0NR	17464	2	–
465011	25.0	48.0NR	17127	2	78
473832	28.1	33.0	13183	2	81
473932	28.1	39.3*	12980	2	80
474032	28.1	43.3*	12875	2	82
474132	28.1	49.4	12843	2	85
474232	28.1	52.5	13001	2	78
474332	28.1	50.7	13023	2	73
474432	28.1	42.3*	13286	2	–
474532	28.4	48.2*	13649	2	–
474632	28.1	52.2	13812	2	95
474732	28.1	52.4*	14285	2	97
474832	28.1	59.0*	13274	2	96
474932	28.1	55.5*	14131	2	98
475032	28.1	53.4*	13685	2	108
475132	28.1	52.8	14542	2	–
475232	28.1	48.0	15063	2	116
484425	25.0	118.7	12417	1	24
484525	25.0	113.5	13764	1	28
484625	25.0	122.6	12598	1	26
484725	25.0	118.0	12620	1	27
484825	25.0	116.8	12321	1	27

(1)	(2)	(3)	(4)	(5)	(6)
484925	25.0	117.2	12258	1	24
485025	25.0	115.0	12309	1	26
485125	25.0	113.2	12288	1	26
485225	25.0	103.9	12073	1	26
485325	25.0	88.8	11825	1	28
493914	20.0	93.9	13824	1	39
494014	20.0	104.9	12716	1	38
494114	20.0	105.1	14483	1	46
494214	20.0	74.9	11798	2	50
494314	20.0	94.4	12610	2	60
494414	20.0	94.0	12790	2	54
494514	20.0	85.2	12979	2	60
494614	20.0	83.3	12957	2	63
494714	20.0	92.5	12792	2	66
494814	20.0	94.0NR	12770	2	–
494914	20.0	87.8	12810	2	72
504114	25.0	40.0NR	13418	2	–
504214	25.0	51.0NR	12554	2	–
504314	25.0	57.0NR	13181	2	–
504414	25.0	67.0NR	13018	2	–
504514	25.0	62.0NR	13685	2	–
504614	25.0	65.0NR	12737	2	–
504714	25.0	80.0NR	12730	2	–
504814	25.0	76.0NR	13047	2	–
504914	25.0	60.0NR	13101	2	–
505014	25.0	76.0NR	12831	2	–
505114	25.0	63.0*	13033	2	60
505214	25.0	74.1	13024	2	72
514525	22.5	94.7*	13011	1	31
514625	22.5	90.7*	12873	1	29
514725	22.5	97.5	12942	1	30
514825	22.5	97.1	12955	1	33
515025	22.5	100.7	12795	2	44
515125	22.5	101.1	12847	2	48
524625	22.5	92.3*	12800	1	32
524825	22.5	91.1	12800	2	40
525025	22.5	99.8	12810	3	55
525125	22.5	98.9	12855	3	57
525225	22.5	100.2	12946	3	57
525325	22.5	94.1	12992	3	57
534816	25.0	83.8*	12047	2	50
534916	25.0	95.0*	12449	2	64
535016	25.0	86.1*	13164	2	60

(1)	(2)	(3)	(4)	(5)	(6)
535116	25.0	94.9*	12650	2	67
535216	25.0	97.6	12534	2	70
544315	25.0	86.8	12502	2	77
544415	25.0	94.3	12485	2	83
544515	25.0	69.7	12632	2	75
544615	25.0	55.0	13096	2	102
554826	25.0	100.9NR	11326	1	22
555026	25.0	88.7	11613	2	30
555126	25.0	90.3	11872	2	30
555226	25.0	77.6	12012	2	31
555326	25.0	68.9NR	12246	2	32
564825	22.5	80.8	12253	1	32
564926	22.5	75.9	12297	1	29
565126	22.5	92.4	12491	2	52
575016	29.3	92.2	12200	1	28
575116	29.3	90.3	12525	1	28
575216	29.3	92.2	12597	1	28
575316	29.3	92.0	12581	1	28
585127	28.3	73.3Δ	12254	1	–
585227	28.3	91.1	12200	1	35
585327	28.3	96.8	12142	1	38
595116	23.0	76.0*	12173	2	35
595216	23.0	80.3	12146	2	35
595316	23.0	78.6	12131	2	36
605317	22.0	36.6Δ	13320	2	–
1374936	22.0	80.0Δ	12262	1	–
1375036	22.0	78.5*	12278	1	29
1375236	22.0	54.4*	12695	2	41
1375336	22.0	62.8	12607	2	42
1525327	20.0	44.0Δ	14970	1	24
614325	35.0	74.3	11961	1	27
614425	35.0	93.0	12033	1	34
614525	35.0	92.5	12416	1	37
614625	35.0	99.4	12206	1	37
614725	35.0	97.8	12295	1	80
623812	36.0	63.6*	14805	2	79
623912	36.0	67.6*	14535	2	80
624012	36.0	57.9*	14628	2	80
624112	36.0	63.5*	14928	2	79
624212	36.0	68.2*	15220	2	72
624312	36.0	72.9*	15242	2	–
624412	36.0	72.1*	15406	2	69
624512	36.0	68.8*	15818	2	73

APPENDIX A

(1)	(2)	(3)	(4)	(5)	(6)
624612	36.0	73.8*	15426	2	76
624712	36.0	69.4*	15434	2	83
624812	36.0	73.5*	15170	2	82
624912	36.0	70.2*	15692	2	85
625012	36.0	66.7*	15729	2	83
625112	36.0	70.5*	15538	2	94
633914	30.0	66.8*	12917	1	45
634014	30.0	77.6	12571	1	–
634114	30.0	86.0	12906	1	–
634214	30.0	84.4	12977	1	–
634314	30.0	86.5	13217	1	–
634414	30.0	86.7	13383	1	62
634514	30.0	85.1	13685	1	60
634614	30.0	85.1	13434	1	62
634714	30.0	88.6	13841	1	62
634814	30.0	87.4	13855	1	60
634914	30.0	79.6	14593	1	56
635014	30.0	77.6	14377	1	51
635114	30.0	79.4	14069	1	60
635214	30.0	75.8	13293	1	55
635314	30.0	67.0*	14053	1	52
643812	33.8	27.8	14211	2	54
643912	33.8	28.0	14175	2	53
644012	33.8	47.3	14182	2	54
644112	33.8	35.6	14558	2	59
644212	33.8	36.8	14754	2	71
644312	33.8	43.8	14977	2	72
644412	33.8	47.4	15527	2	70
644512	33.8	42.8	15753	2	–
644612	33.8	47.7	15653	2	–
644712	33.8	55.3	15841	2	96
644812	33.8	55.8	15974	2	102
654615	30.0	97.0	13497	1	48
654715	30.0	104.8*	13097	1	49
654815	30.0	110.0NR	13093	1	–
654915	30.0	105.7	13412	1	50
655115	30.0	98.8	13118	2	64
655215	30.0	79.2	13277	2	64
655315	30.0	77.6	13168	2	63
663812	35.0	38.6	14354	4	165
663912	35.0	47.1	14363	4	168
664012	35.0	56.9	14526	4	178
664112	35.0	68.3	14597	4	191

(1)	(2)	(3)	(4)	(5)	(6)
664212	35.0	64.7	14713	4	219
674014	35.0	84.2	11393	1	60
674114	35.0	89.9	11909	1	52
674214	35.0	100.5	11924	1	51
674314	35.0	91.1	11895	1	50
674414	35.0	83.6	11640	1	–
674515	35.0	97.2	11574	1	52
674614	35.0	99.8	11697	1	59
674714	35.0	105.3	11706	1	65
683924	31.3	69.8	13951	1	57
684024	31.3	75.1	13490	1	52
684124	31.3	78.7*	13435	1	59
684224	31.3	70.1*	14179	1	62
684324	31.3	90.4*	13437	1	56
684424	31.3	96.3*	13306	1	50
694425	37.5	96.9*	12757	1	36
694525	37.5	94.9*	12783	1	23
494625	37.5	92.3*	12837	1	26
694825	37.5	90.3	12872	2	33
694925	37.5	79.3*	13046	2	26
704826	30.0	79.1Δ	12135	1	–
704926	30.0	95.4	11894	1	45
705126	30.0	83.7	11824	3	67
705226	30.0	92.8	11997	3	–
715116	30.0	108.5	11964	2	65
715216	30.0	106.6	12297	2	66
715316	30.0	109.0	12137	2	68
725126	30.0	64.3	12182	2	30
725326	30.0	96.0	12142	3	36
735026	30.0	31.6Δ	14123	1	–
735126	30.0	44.6	13789	1	40
735226	30.0	47.2	13401	1	36
735326	30.0	53.7	13382	1	26
745236	30.0	60.7	11766	3	79
745336	30.0	79.9	11483	3	–
755016	34.5	68.2	13891	1	28
755116	34.5	77.9	13239	1	24
755216	34.5	76.1	13534	1	24
755316	34.5	69.1	13169	1	28
765127	30.0	73.0Δ	12373	1	–
765227	30.0	69.6*	11943	1	29
765327	30.0	75.2NR	11782	1	34
775122	35.0	38.3*	18824	2	83

(1)	(2)	(3)	(4)	(5)	(6)
775222	35.0	90.3*	16062	2	70
785227	30.0	76.5Δ	12713	1	–
785327	30.0	94.4	12008	1	23
795336	35.0	99.7	14049	1	27
805327	30.0	70.4Δ*	11851	1	–
1384916	30.0	106.4	13017	1	48
1385016	30.0	104.9*	12260	1	48
1385136	30.0	105.8	12090	1	48
1395016	34.5	99.4	11970	2	61
1395116	34.5	98.8	12077	2	67
1395216	34.5	102.7	11987	2	68
1395316	34.5	100.5	11896	2	68
1535327	33.0	67.0Δ	11743	1	–
814234	40.0	91.1	11928	1	63
814434	40.0	89.3	12739	2	70
814534	40.0	87.1	12649	2	72
814634	40.0	82.0	12576	2	74
814734	40.0	89.0	12356	2	72
814834	40.0	90.9	12446	2	76
814934	40.0	88.8	12404	2	75
815034	40.0	99.3	12452	2	77
824234	40.0	69.9*	12870	2	60
824434	40.0	82.9	12551	3	99
824534	40.0	77.0	12525	3	98
824634	40.0	57.0	12581	3	107
824734	20.0	80.7	12087	3	118
824934	40.0	58.3	12501	4	135
825034	40.0	76.4	11983	4	149
825134	40.0	79.7	12460	4	147
825234	40.0	75.2	12641	4	150
825334	40.0	71.0	12891	4	142
833811	50.0	29.1	14000	6	271
833911	50.0	24.4	14140	6	268
834011	50.0	29.5	14000	6	266
834111	50.0	38.6	14100	6	281
834211	50.0	31.9	14100	6	298
834311	50.0	39.4	13960	6	292
834411	50.0	41.0	14050	5	281
834511	50.0	32.4	14240	6	294
834611	50.0	35.9	14040	6	343
834711	50.0	44.5	14400	6	399
834811	50.0	47.7	14420	6	414
843812	55.0	74.1	12500	1	70

(1)	(2)	(3)	(4)	(5)	(6)
843912	55.0	73.5	12631	1	76
844012	55.0	79.6	12425	1	73
844112	55.0	81.5	12505	1	75
844212	55.0	78.8*	12619	1	74
844312	55.0	82.3	12545	1	74
844412	55.0	81.4	12358	1	72
844512	55.0	78.2	12458	1	–
844612	55.0	74.3	12579	1	–
844712	55.0	84.5	12419	1	78
844812	55.0	81.3	12591	1	79
854114	40.0	80.7	11692	2	91
854214	40.0	76.5	11656	2	98
854314	40.0	78.6	11814	2	94
854414	40.0	63.9	11787	2	93
854514	40.0	67.7*	11749	2	85
854614	40.0	71.5*	11765	2	86
854714	40.0	77.9*	11753	2	85
863912	50.0	44.3	13580	4	175
864012	50.0	48.6	13455	4	175
864112	50.0	58.4	13647	4	183
864212	50.0	56.3	13697	4	196
864312	50.0	66.4	14140	4	177
864412	50.0	72.5	14486	4	184
864512	50.0	66.6	14527	4	189
864612	50.0	60.8	14184	4	206
864712	50.0	71.6	14427	4	208
864812	50.0	77.5	14413	4	219
864912	50.0	72.7	14354	4	218
865012	50.0	51.8	14472	4	214
865112	50.0	60.7	14569	4	208
865212	50.0	60.5	14647	4	214
865312	50.0	60.8	14766	4	205
874415	50.0	98.9*	13700	1	–
874515	50.0	113.6	12309	1	81
874615	50.0	105.9	12611	1	108
874815	50.0	113.9	12362	2	138
874915	50.0	101.1	12486	2	146
883812	50.0	85.8	14350	2	180
883912	50.0	87.4	14249	2	176
884012	50.0	83.8*	14059	2	176
884112	50.0	87.0	14071	2	182
884212	50.0	87.2	14057	2	194
884312	50.0	86.4	14135	2	202

APPENDIX A

(1)	(2)	(3)	(4)	(5)	(6)
884412	50.0	89.1	13828	2	196
884512	50.0	87.2	13774	2	192
884612	50.0	88.4	13847	2	191
884712	50.0	90.2	13767	2	191
884812	50.0	87.9	13881	2	196
884912	50.0	85.1	13969	2	195
885012	50.0	71.7	14178	2	195
885112	50.0	65.4	14474	2	194
885212	50.0	63.9	14429	2	195
894515	50.0	93.3	12058	1	59
894615	50.0	88.3	11950	1	81
894715	50.0	104.8	11921	1	81
894815	50.0	101.0NR	11871	1	81
904916	50.0	63.0NR	11608	2	–
905016	50.0	87.0NR	11530	2	–
905116	50.0	75.8*	11613	2	80
905216	50.0	81.9	11697	2	80
905316	50.0	83.6	11720	2	81
915136	40.0	84.9	11427	3	–
915236	40.0	89.8	11331	3	112
915336	40.0	103.9	11224	3	122
925236	44.0	66.3	12441	3	40
925336	44.0	80.0	12418	3	41
935026	44.0	73.4	11283	2	–
935126	44.0	105.8	11345	2	38
935226	44.0	111.8	11481	2	38
945036	46.0	83.6*	11366	1	64
945136	46.0	81.3	11155	1	65
955036	50.0	82.8Δ	11951	1	–
955236	50.0	92.7	11944	2	46
955336	50.0	90.3	12287	2	47
965016	44.0	55.1Δ*	13131	1	–
965116	44.0	48.9*	13399	1	34
965216	44.0	55.6*	13171	1	33
965316	44.0	55.1*	13177	1	37
975127	40.0	95.6*	11044	1	–
975227	40.0	97.7*	11000	1	38
985116	40.0	101.3	11168	2	60
985216	40.0	96.7	11470	2	60
985316	40.0	97.9	11397	2	59
995127	46.0	91.8Δ	12109	1	–
995227	46.0	94.7	12101	1	27
1005227	44.0	94.5Δ	12029	1	–

(1)	(2)	(3)	(4)	(5)	(6)
1005327	44.0	102.7*	12064	1	33
1025327	40.0	69.7	12226	1	55
1405116	46.0	56.9	11923	6	–
1405216	46.0	63.6	11959	5	148
1405316	46.0	69.9	12153	5	160
1414916	40.0	82.1Δ*	11405	1	–
1415216	40.0	81.1	11388	3	80
1424936	44.0	93.9NR	11116	1	50
1425136	44.0	74.1	11009	2	87
1425236	44.0	85.2	10909	2	62
1425336	44.0	77.2*	11019	2	71
1434916	40.0	101.1	10892	1	–
1435016	40.0	110.7	10941	1	47
1444916	50.0	94.1Δ*	11544	1	–
1445016	50.0	106.4	11365	1	56
1445116	50.0	110.4*	11177	1	52
1445216	50.0	102.6*	11735	1	55
1445316	50.0	106.4*	11399	1	49
1034425	65.0	68.1*	11685	1	80
1034525	65.0	14.0*	15922	1	84
1034625	65.0	18.6*	15082	1	100
1034725	65.0	91.2*	11830	1	96
1034825	65.0	37.9*	12412	2	126
1043812	68.0	60.5*	13302	1	–
1043912	68.0	58.5	13405	1	–
1044012	68.0	62.7*	13191	1	–
1044112	68.0	66.1	13152	1	101
1044212	68.0	70.0*	13036	1	109
1044312	68.0	60.0*	12960	1	107
1044412	68.0	71.7*	13106	1	100
1044512	68.0	70.4*	13287	1	99
1044612	68.0	65.4*	13214	1	102
1044712	68.0	65.8	13183	1	106
1044812	68.0	68.2	13321	1	106
1044912	68.0	67.3	13472	1	124
1054315	60.0	84.9*	11529	1	–
1054515	60.0	71.3*	11792	2	83
1054615	60.0	74.6*	11716	2	96
1054715	60.0	78.2*	11571	2	95
1054915	60.0	75.2	11758	3	102
1055015	60.0	71.4	11593	3	102
1064315	66.0	82.4	12100	1	81
1064415	66.0	102.2	12451	1	73

APPENDIX A

(1)	(2)	(3)	(4)	(5)	(6)
1064515	66.0	104.6	12487	1	69
1064615	66.0	104.9	12395	1	74
1064715	66.0	108.4	12247	1	74
1064815	66.0	106.6	12473	1	75
1074215	60.0	76.0	11700	2	124
1074415	60.0	87.7	11290	3	107
1074615	60.0	42.1	11900	4	124
1074815	60.0	90.4	11611	4	254
1074915	60.0	82.4	11260	4	270
1075015	60.0	65.6	11215	4	281
1075115	60.0	88.2*	11122	4	229
1075215	60.0	89.3	11118	4	236
1075315	60.0	92.1	11161	4	230
1085227	66.0	67.0	11290	2	45
1085327	66.0	74.1	10949	2	45
1095237	60.0	89.4	10859	2	95
1095337	60.0	89.7	10879	2	99
1105127	66.0	63.2Δ	12390	1	–
1105227	66.0	67.8	11874	1	31
1105327	66.0	63.1	11839	1	34
1115217	66.0	82.9*	11439	1	–
1115317	66.0	75.4*	11712	1	39
1125227	66.0	62.3	13232	1	30
1125327	66.0	54.7	12591	1	26
1135217	60.0	92.6*	9794	1	52
1135317	60.0	103.2*	9942	1	63
1145227	69.0	57.4	12047	1	33
1145327	69.0	69.2	11595	1	31
1155317	75.0	73.1	10304	1	–
1455036	69.0	87.3*	11959	2	102
1455136	69.0	89.6*	11985	2	102
1455236	69.0	85.3*	12033	2	102
1455336	69.0	84.4*	12119	2	100
1464916	66.0	71.2*	11143	2	70
1465116	66.0	68.0	11213	3	89
1465216	66.0	68.8	11150	3	80
1465316	66.0	67.9	11243	3	81
1474916	60.0	90.2NR	11555	1	–
1475016	60.0	96.0NR	11616	1	73
1475216	60.0	91.5	11549	2	90
1475316	60.0	79.0	11718	2	90
1555327	73.5	82.0Δ	12007	1	–
1565327	65.0	102.6Δ	11418	1	–

(1)	(2)	(3)	(4)	(5)	(6)
1575327	79.6	88.0Δ	11386	1	–
1585337	69.0	82.0	10873	1	31
1595317	69.0	101.9	11511	2	43
1164615	100.0	80.1	11466	1	73
1164715	100.0	97.3	11190	1	85
1173813	80.0	61.7*	10788	1	63
1173913	80.0	63.5	10770	1	69
1174013	80.0	69.8	10729	1	82
1174113	80.0	75.2	10606	1	91
1174213	80.0	74.3	10596	1	105
1174313	80.0	70.7	11236	1	109
1185116	70.0	97.0*	10642	2	74
1185216	70.0	93.7*	10802	2	78
1185316	70.0	87.0*	10640	2	81
1195316	152.5	82.3	9594	4	247
1205316	75.0	86.8	12382	2	132
1215116	80.0	83.8	10918	2	77
1215216	80.0	86.1	10985	2	80
1215316	80.0	89.5	11050	2	82
1225136	100.0	87.9	10986	2	99
1225336	100.0	77.6	11198	3	134
1235236	150.0	80.5	10751	2	178
1245337	81.9	74.9*	9972	2	118
1255227	80.3	60.9Δ	11934	1	–
1255327	80.3	71.7	11587	1	33
1665217	100.0	81.3Δ	10272	1	–
1265116	80.0	98.2	9540	2	83
1265216	80.0	98.4	9430	2	92
1265316	80.0	104.2	9510	2	100
1275217	75.0	93.3*	9840	2	–
1285237	90.0	99.8*	9971	2	78
1285337	90.0	99.3	10151	2	81
1485026	110.0	83.2	10389	3	136
1495016	74.8	82.3	11530	2	96
1495115	74.8	88.4	11472	2	80
1495216	74.8	89.0	11457	2	83
1495316	74.8	82.2	11491	2	85
1615337	100.0	91.1	10109	1	–
1655317	100.0	80.6Δ	9864	1	–

APPENDIX B

Data used for the estimation of the capital-input functions

Plant number	Number of machines in plant	Total capital cost ($1 000)	Total equipment cost ($1 000)
(i) Coal plants 1945–50			
16	2	1 671	1 183
22	1	1 816	1 317
131	2	3 212	2 484
132	1	1 623	1 196
34	2	5 381	3 435
40	1	3 535	2 423
53	2	8 440	5 162
57	1	6 301	4 463
59	2	7 001	5 342
71	2	9 796	6 970
75	1	7 301	4 187
138	1	6 107	3 886
139	2	11 445	7 707
90	2	14 521	10 119
140	5	29 019	21 000
144	1	11 491	7 508
146	3	23 140	16 245
147	2	19 507	14 436
118	2	14 441	11 390
119	4	60 529	48 921
121	2	23 313	18 029
126	2	25 642	19 508
149	2	27 945	18 573
(ii) Mixed plants 1945–50			
10	2	1 396	1 033
31	1	5 323	3 127

Plant number	Number of machines in plant	Total capital cost ($1 000)	Total equipment cost ($1 000)
32	1	5 332	3 929
35	2	4 271	3 166
133	2	4 753	3 255
137	2	7 985	5 567
74	3	19 524	13 505
79	1	8 189	5 989
138	1	6 107	3 886
91	3	29 944	18 843
92	3	19 639	16 703
94	1	9 970	6 650
95	2	14 541	11 723
142	2	18 518	12 265
145	2	12 152	9 531
122	3	30 201	24 546
123	4	124 280	88 828
23	1	2 068	1 471
134	2	5 083	3 637

(iii) Non-coal plants 1951–53

Plant number	Number of machines in plant	Total capital cost ($1 000)	Total equipment cost ($1 000)
19	1	930	857
21	2	1 724	1 385
150	1	783	655
151	3	3 716	3 323
58	1	5 177	4 072
152	1	3 640	3 070
78	1	4 160	3 513
80	2	11 665	9 290
153	2	7 428	6 331
97	3	18 385	14 484
99	2	10 510	8 489
100	1	6 869	5 115
102	1	8 326	5 997
108	2	13 656	10 321
110	1	6 854	5 065
112	1	5 669	4 941
114	1	9 877	7 553
155	1	8 852	7 627
125	2	7 491	5 993

Note: Source FPC Reports. For plant identification see Appendix C.

APPENDIX C

Plant identification

Plant number	Name	State
1	Rio Pecos	Texas
2	Dawson	New Mexico
3	Jowett	Texas
4	Minnesota Valley	Minnesota
5	Williston	North Dakota
6	Rapid City	South Dakota
7	French Island	Wisconsin
8	Cedar	Utah
9	Guymon	Oklahoma
10	Trinidad	Colorado
11	Dodge City no. 2	Kansas
12	Tucson	Arizona
13	Lawrence	Kansas
14	James De Young	Michigan
15	Whitney	Minnesota
16	Menasha	Wisconsin
17	Jim Bullock	Colorado
19	Elk City	Oklahoma
20	Colby no. 2	Kansas
22	Ishpeming	Michigan
23	H. Newman	Missouri
24	Santa Fe	New Mexico
25	Brantley	Virginia
26	Pineville	Kentucky
27	English	Connecticut
28	Inglis	Florida
29	Riverside	Kansas
30	Mason	Maine
31	Arthur Kill	New York
32	Sabrooke	Illinois

Plant number	Name	State
34	Red Wing	Minnesota
35	Fox Lake	Minnesota
36	Avon Park	Florida
37	Pauline	Texas
38	Lincoln Beerbower	Oklahoma
39	Provo	Utah
40	Ortonville	Minnesota
41	Ripley	Kansas
42	Manchester	New Hampshire
43	Buckport no. 2	Maine
44	Sarasota	Florida
45	Beaver Channel	Iowa
46	Grand Tower	Illinois
47	South Amboy	New Jersey
48	Harvey Couch	Arkansas
49	Greenidge	New York
50	Hutsonville	Illinois
51	Pensacola	Florida
52	Eaton	Mississippi
53	Tyrone	Kentucky
54	Paddy's Run	Kentucky
55	Lieberman	Louisiana
56	Hagood	South Carolina
57	Suburban High Pressure	Pennsylvania
58	Palatka	Florida
59	Milesburg	Pennsylvania
60	Bridgeport	Iowa
61	Silver Gate	California
62	Gould Street	Maryland
63	Cumberland High Pressure	Maryland
64	Raritan River	New Jersey
65	Jennison	New York
66	Avon	Ohio
67	New Castle	Pennsylvania
68	Mountain Creek	Texas
69	West Junction	Texas
70	Hookers Point	Florida
71	Green River	Kentucky
72	Knox Lee	Texas
73	Jim Hill	Missouri
74	Harold Kramer	Nebraska
75	Riverton	Virginia

Plant number	Name	State
76	Laredo	Texas
77	Shuffleton	Washington
78	Kyrene	Arizona
79	Zuni	Colorado
80	Suwannee River	Florida
81	Chickasaw	Alabama
82	Arkwright	Georgia
83	Trenton Channel	Michigan
84	Gilbert	New Jersey
85	Cliffside	North Carolina
86	Ashtabula	Ohio
87	R.E. Burger	Ohio
88	Stanton	Pennsylvania
89	Chesterfield	Virginia
90	Meredosia	Illinois
91	Wood River	Illinois
92	Arapahoe	Colorado
93	Lake Catherine	Arkansas
94	West Springfield	Massachusetts
95	Mustang	Oklahoma
96	Hale no. 2	Utah
97	Higgins	Florida
98	Riverwood	Indiana
99	Sweatt	Mississippi
100	Murray Gill	Kansas
102	McManus	Georgia
103	Harbor	California
104	Michigan City	Indiana
105	Riverside	Maryland
106	F. R. Phillips	Pennsylvania
107	Watts Bar	Tennessee
108	Hamilton Moses	Arkansas
109	Edge Moor	Delaware
110	Natchez	Mississippi
111	Black Dog	Minnesota
112	Frank Bird	Montana
113	Danskammer	New York
114	Gadsby no. 1	Utah
115	Hennepin	Illinois
116	Tidd	Ohio
117	Port Washington	Wisconsin
118	Dan River	North Carolina

Plant number	Name	State
119	Philip Sporn	West Virginia
120	Sunbury	Pennsylvania
121	Potomac River	Virginia
122	Yates	Georgia
123	Ridgeland	Illinois
124	Salem Harbour	Massachusetts
125	Southwestern	Oklahoma
126	Dunkirk	New York
127	Titus	Pennsylvania
128	W.S. Lee	South Carolina
129	New Johnsonville	Tennessee
130	Wabash	Indiana
131	Crookston	Minnesota
132	Hoot Lake	Minnesota
133	Wilmarth	Minnesota
134	Lawrence	South Dakota
135	Permian Basin	Texas
137	Hudson	New York
138	Hickling	New York
139	Warren	Pennsylvania
140	Havana	Illinois
141	White River	Indiana
142	Port Jefferson	New York
143	Russell	New York
144	Willow Island	West Virginia
145	Gadsden	Alabama
146	B.C. Cobb	Michigan
147	Possum Point	Virginia
148	Sewaren	New Jersey
149	Mitchell	Pennsylvania
150	Fort Stockton	Texas
152	Teche	Louisiana
153	Paint Creek	Texas
155	Arbuckle	Oklahoma
156	Parkdale	Texas
157	Lake Creek	Texas
158	Gadsby no. 2	New York
159	Albright	West Virginia
161	Glenwood no. 3	New York
165	Portsmouth	Virginia
166	W.C. Beckjord	Ohio

APPENDIX D

The measure of capacity utilisation when machines in a plant operate for different hours hot and connected: analysis of the one-machine plant sample

This Appendix discusses certain problems arising from the derivation of measures of capacity utilisation of machines obtained in chapter 3, when these results are related to the optimal use of plant which is discussed in the Appendix to chapter 3. A special subsample of the data used to obtain the results in chapter 5 is employed here to estimate the T-period models obtained from models A and B of chapter 5, in order to avoid certain of these problems arising from the measure of capacity utilisation.

In chapter 3 equation (3.13) we derived a correct measure of capacity utilisation for the plant as a whole

$$C_3 = PF^* = \frac{\sum\limits_{i=1}^{M} \sum\limits_{j=1}^{t_{1i}} X_{ij}}{\sum\limits_{i=1}^{M} t_{1i} X_{Ki}} \qquad (D.1)$$

where there are M machines in the plant, X_{Ki} is the size (maximum hourly output) of the ith machine, X_{ij} is the output produced in the jth hour on the ith machine and t_{1i} is the number of hours during the year when the ith machine operates hot and connected to load.

We shall only consider the sample of plants composed of machines of the same size and vintage. Thus in this case we have from (D.1),

$$PF^* = \frac{\sum\limits_{i=1}^{M} \sum\limits_{j=1}^{t_{1i}} X_{ij}}{X_K \sum\limits_{i=1}^{M} t_{1i}} \qquad (D.2)$$

where X_K is the common size of machines in the plant.

Two assumptions were made, p. 41, which enabled PF* in (D.2) to be estimated from the published PF and then to be used as the common level of capacity utilisation for each machine in the plant *on a yearly basis.*

Assumption (i) stated that $t_{1i} = t_1$ for $i = 1, ..., M$, where t_1 is the published hours that the plant operates hot and connected to load, i.e. when at least one machine operates hot and connected. Thus on the basis of this assumption (D.2) becomes (equation (3.15))

$$\text{PF}^* = \frac{\sum_{i=1}^{M} \sum_{j=1}^{t_{1i}} X_{ij}}{t_1 \cdot M \cdot X_K} \tag{D.3}$$

which is estimated from the published data.

(D.3) is a capacity utilisation variable for the plant as a whole and it is stated that it will be an underestimate of the degree of capacity utilisation for the plant (p. 40) if not all machines operate in each hour when the plant is operated hot and connected.

In order to use (D.3) as a measure of the degree of capacity utilisation on each machine assumption (ii) is made which states that over the year the output on each machine is the same. The rationale given for this is that the plant operator wishes to spread the degree of depreciation (implicitly considered as a function of utilisation) over machines. On the basis of assumption (ii) the measure of capacity utilisation for an individual machine *over the year* is obtained from (D.3):

$$\text{PF}^* = \frac{M \sum_{j=1}^{t_1} X_j}{t_1 \cdot M \cdot X_K} = \frac{\sum_{j=1}^{t_1} X_j}{t_1 X_K} \tag{D.4}$$

where $\sum_{j=1}^{t_1} X_j$ is the common output on any machine over the year.

We must now relate these results to the appendix to chapter 3 which discussed the optimal use of machines. It was shown there that in any unit time period (an hour for the purposes of this analysis) as many machines as possible will be used at full capacity and the remaining output produced on any other machine. Thus the typical *hourly* rate of capacity utilisation will be 100 per cent, however, the yearly rate can vary. As long as the assumptions (i) and (ii) hold, the derived PF* of (D.3) will measure the degree of capacity utilisation of a machine over the year whether the plant operator is following the optimisation procedure or not. However, it is likely that if the plant operator does optimise in the use of machines, assumption (i) will be violated and the measure in (D.3) will be an under-estimate of the correct degree of capacity utilisation of individual machines.

Consider the following examples: suppose there is a plant composed of two 100 MW machines of the same vintage.

(a) Let the demand pattern be 130 MW continuous over 8 760 hours. Then provided that assumption (ii) holds and the plant operator optimises, each machine operates for 4 380 hours at 100 per cent capacity and 4 380 hours at 30 per cent capacity. Hence the direct measure of capacity utilisation for each machine is given by

$$\frac{4\,380 \times 100 + 4\,380 \times 30}{8\,760 \times 100} \times 100 \text{ per cent}$$

$$= 65 \text{ per cent}.$$

While if we use (D.3) we have that

$$PF^* = \frac{2\,[4\,380 \times 100 + 4\,380 \times 30]}{100 \times 2 \times 8\,760} \times 100 \text{ per cent}$$

$$= 65 \text{ per cent}.$$

Hence in this case PF* from (D.3) is the correct measure of capacity utilisation when the plant operator optimises his use of machines. This is because assumptions (i) and (ii) hold.

(b) Consider now that demand in the first 4 380 hours is for an output of 100 MW continuous, while in the second 4 380 hours it is for 130 MW continuous. Then if the plant operator optimises and assumption (ii) holds, each machine operates at

    100 per cent for 2 190 hours in the first 4 380 hours

    100 per cent for 2 190 hours in the second 4 380 hours

    30 per cent for 2 190 hours in the second 4 380 hours.

Then the direct measure of capacity utilisation of each machine is given by

$$\frac{(100 \times 2\,190) + (100 \times 2\,190) + (30 \times 2\,190)}{3 \times 2\,190 \times 100} \times 100 \text{ per cent}$$

$$= 76.67 \text{ per cent}.$$

The individual machine measure of capacity derived from (D.3) is given by

$$\frac{2\,[230 \times 2\,190]}{8\,760 \times 2 \times 100} \times 100 \text{ per cent}$$

$$= 57.5 \text{ per cent}$$

which of course is an underestimate of the true degree of capacity operation of each machine because although at least one machine operates for 8 760 hours both do not, and thus assumption (i) is violated.

(c) As a final and even simpler example, consider that demand is for 100 MW continuous in each hour. Then on the basis of assumption (ii) and the optimisation procedure each machine operates for 4 380 hours at 100 per cent capacity. But the degree of capacity utilisation derived from (D.3) is

$$\frac{100 \times 8\,760}{100 \times 2 \times 8\,760} \times 100 \text{ per cent}$$

$$= 50 \text{ per cent}.$$

We see then that when hourly demand falls below the capacity size of the machine in the plant the optimisation procedure implies that only one machine is utilised, and hence assumption (i) would be violated, and the degree of capacity operation of each machine is underestimated.

In order to avoid this problem and to determine whether the extent of underestimation of capacity utilisation of machines had a serious effect on the results presented in chapter 5, a further analysis was carried out considering only those plants which had a single machine. For plants with only one machine (D.3) reduces to

$$\frac{\sum_{j=1}^{t_1} X_j}{t_1 X_K} \qquad\qquad (D.5)$$

which is the desired capacity utilisation rate of a machine on a yearly basis.

The T-period equations derived from models A and B were fitted to a subsample of the data composed of those plants which had only one machine. The size of the sample is shown in table D.1 and the estimated equations are presented in tables D.2 and D.3 respectively.

As in chapter 5, model B will be accepted as the ex-post production function although for the sample of one-machine plants its advantages over model A appear less obvious than for the full sample. But for purposes of analysis we shall proceed by accepting model B as the ex-post production function.

A comparison of table D.3 with table 5.4, which presents the results of model B for the full sample, shows the following:

(1) $\hat{\alpha}$ is greater for the one-machine plants except for the 1930–39 non-coal plants. This means that for the one-machine plants the ex-post production function is somewhat steeper than for the complete sample of plants. Thus the degree of intra-capacity economies is greater when the ex-post production function was estimated for one-machine plants.

(2) $\hat{\beta}$ is very similar for non-coal plants in the two estimations but varies somewhat for coal and mixed plants.

(3) $\hat{\gamma}$ is uniformly smaller for coal and mixed plants in the one-machine estimation and similar in both cases for the non-coal plants. These results are also presented in figures D.1 and D.2.

TABLE D.1

Size of sample of one-machine plants

Vintage	Coal and mixed observations	plants	Non-coal observations	plants
1925–29	46	4	41	3
1930–39	76	9	89	9
1940–44	31	8	31	7
1945–50	64	23	15	5
1951–53	11	8	35	20

Table D.2

T-period regressions derived from model A for the sample of one-machine plants.

Model A: $a_{it} = \alpha \left(\dfrac{X_{it}}{X_{iK}} \right)^{-1} + \beta(X_{iK}) + \gamma + v_{it}$

Vintage	$\hat{\alpha}$	$\hat{\beta}$	$\hat{\gamma}$	$\bar{R}^2$
(i) Coal and mixed plants				
1925–29	621144.6	−141.1	12732.4	0.8242
	(104750.2)	(10.2)	(1485.0)	
1930–39	432373.9	−91.1	11250.0	0.7354
	(54919.1)	(7.5)	(740.4)	
1940–44	750218.0	−97.9	10429.0	0.7317
	(186779.5)	(20.9)	(2782.3)	
1945–50	238670.0	−72.9	12312.1	0.7884
	(38399.7)	(6.5)	(583.1)	
1951–53	434362.2***	−36.1	8171.0	0.8310
	(158344.9)	(5.9)	(2001.5)	
(ii) Non-coal plants				
1925–29	196977.9	−536.6	22741.1	0.9523
	(53790.0)	(24.8)	(1012.6)	
1930–39	223808.9	−275.0	16718.3	0.6815
	(30051.7)	(37.3)	(817.2)	
1940–44	66558.0	−15.1***	12208.4	0.7431
	(7836.6)	(7.0)	(192.0)	
1945–50	158772.9	−190.0	15401.2	0.8809
	(34224.1)	(18.9)	(411.5)	
1951–53	226676.4	−46.0	11531.3	0.6041
	(54919.2)	(9.0)	(958.7)	

Note: ***, implies not significantly different from zero at the 1 per cent levels.

TABLE D.3

T-period regressions derived from model B for the
sample of one-machine plants

Model B: $a_{it} = \alpha \left(\dfrac{X_{it}}{X_{iK}}\right)^{-1} + \beta(X_{iK})^{-1} + \gamma + v_{it}$

Vintage	$\hat{\alpha}$	$\hat{\beta}$	$\hat{\gamma}$	$\bar{R}^2$
(i) Coal and mixed plants				
1925–29	71267.3***	43453.5	11275.5	0.9874
	(28882.3)	(765.2)	(392.4)	
1930–39	279800.5	38852.5	8669.2	0.9451
	(79676.7)	(5979.9)	(986.1)	
1940–44	341847.2	28190.5	8529.0	0.9443
	(93608.6)	(1931.7)	(1009.5)	
1945–50	209229.1	26052.8	9201.3	0.7694
	(41212.0)	(2477.8)	(500.2)	
1951–53	308609.5**	16411.0	6587.4	0.8414
	(157291.5)	(2565.2)	(1872.7)	
(ii) Non-coal plants				
1925–29	359158.5	59505.9	7565.3	0.9175
	(66325.7)	(3724.9)	(891.2)	
1930–39	216710.7	22702.8	10011.8	0.9221
	(14215.6)	(1027.0)	(284.5)	
1940–44	58629.8	5747.5*	11628.2	0.7093
	(7115.2)	(6481.9)	(310.8)	
1945–50	134555.2	26552.5	9488.3	0.9543
	(20027.5)	(1580.7)	(410.1)	
1951–53	121712.5	29294.1	9724.1	0.8864
	(31365.8)	(2246.4)	(428.9)	

Note: *, **, ***, imply not significantly different from zero at the 10, 5 and 1 per cent
levels respectively.

TABLE D.4

Economies of scale: one-machine plants

Size X_K	Vintage 1925–29	1930–39	1940–44	1945–50	1951–53
(i) Coal and mixed machines					
5	20679	19238	17586	16504	12956
	(=100)	(=100)	(=100)	(=100)	(=100)
10	78.99	79.80	83.97	84.21	87.33
20	68.48	69.71	75.95	76.32	81.00
30	64.98	66.34	73.28	73.69	78.89
40	63.23	64.66	71.95	72.38	77.83
50	62.18	63.65	71.15	71.59	77.20
60	61.48	62.97	70.61	71.06	76.78
80	60.60	62.13	69.94	70.40	76.25
100	60.07	61.63	69.54	70.01	75.93
(ii) Non-coal machines					
5	23058	16719	13364	16144	16800
	(=100)	(=100)	(=100)	(=100)	(=100)
10	74.19	86.42	95.69	83.55	82.56
20	61.29	79.63	93.55	75.33	73.84
30	56.99	77.37	92.83	72.59	70.94
40	54.84	76.24	92.47	71.22	69.49
50	53.55	75.56	92.26	70.40	68.61
60	52.69	75.11	92.12	69.85	68.03
80	51.61	74.54	91.94	69.16	67.31
100	50.97	74.20	91.83	68.75	66.87

Note: X_K is size of machine in megawatts. The table measures a_K which is input of fuel per kilowatthour at capacity. Thus

$$a_K = \left(\frac{\hat{\alpha}}{100} + \hat{\gamma}\right) + \frac{\hat{\beta}}{X_K}$$

derived from model B. The row of 5 MW measures a_K in BTU's; the remaining rows measure a_K as an index with the fuel input at capacity for a 5 MW machine set equal to 100 in each vintage column.

TABLE D.5

Technological change: one-machine plants

Size X_K	1925–29(= 100)	1930–39	Vintage 1940–44	1945–50	1951–53
(i) Coal and mixed machines					
5	20679	93.03	85.04	79.81	62.65
10	16334	93.99	90.40	85.09	69.27
20	14161	94.70	94.32	88.95	74.11
30	13437	95.00	95.91	90.51	76.06
40	13075	95.14	96.77	91.36	77.13
50	12857	95.23	97.30	91.89	77.79
60	12712	95.30	97.68	92.25	78.25
80	12531	95.38	98.15	92.72	78.83
100	12423	95.44	98.44	93.01	79.19
(ii) Non-coal machines					
5	23058	72.50	57.96	70.02	72.86
10	17107	84.46	71.40	78.85	81.08
20	14132	94.21	88.46	86.06	87.78
30	13140	98.44	94.41	89.18	90.69
40	12645	100.81	97.74	90.93	92.32
50	12347	102.32	99.86	92.05	93.36
60	12149	103.36	101.33	92.82	94.08
80	11901	104.72	103.24	93.82	95.01
100	11752	105.56	104.43	94.45	95.59

Note: Derived from the estimates of model B. The second column (vintage 1925–29) shows input of fuel per kilowatthour at capacity, a_K, in BTU's. The remaining columns show a_K as an index with the 1925–29 value set equal to 100 in each row.

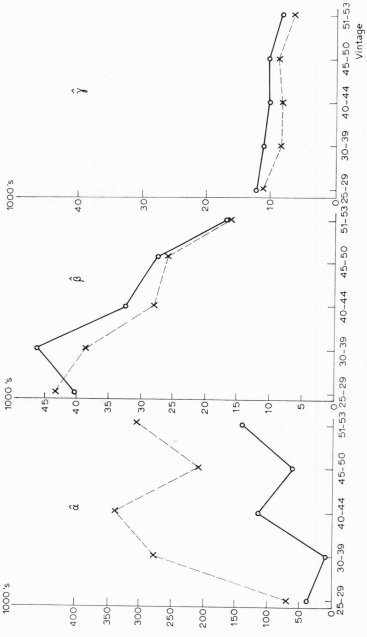

Figure D.1. A comparison of the estimated parameters of model B for the one-machine sample and the total sample. Coal and mixed plants. o: Estimates for the total sample; ×: Estimates for the one-machine sample.

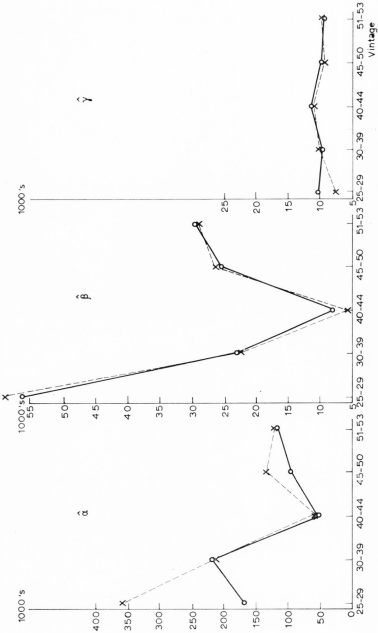

Figure D.2. A comparison of the estimated parameters of model B for the one-machine sample and the total sample. Non-coal plants. o: Estimates for the total sample; x: Estimates for the one-machine sample.

TABLE D.6

Range of the sample of one-machine plants

	Coal and mixed	Non-coal
1925–29	4.00– 68.00	6.50–20.00
1930–39	7.50– 80.00	2.00–31.25
1940–44	2.50–100.00	15.00–65.00
1945–50	7.50– 60.00	5.00–30.00
1951–53	5.00–100.00	5.00–79.60

In order to compare fully the estimation of model B over both samples the analyses presented in tables 5.6 and 5.8 of economies of scale and technological change were carried out for the estimates of model B obtained from the one-machine sample. These are presented in tables D.4 and D.5 respectively. In addition the range of the one machine sample is given in table D.6.

A comparison of tables D.4 and 5.6 shows that the degree of scale economies appears very similar in the two analyses. In the one-machine sample as well as in the total sample the degree of scale economies decreases for coal and mixed machines over time, but this is not evident for non-coal machines.

When we compare tables D.5 and 5.8 to detect any difference in the estimation of technological change, however, certain differences do appear. For the coal and mixed machines over the period 1925–29 to 1951–53 the reduction in fuel requirements attributed to technological change seems about the same in the two estimations. However, for non-coal machines this was not the case. For the one-machine estimation the effect of technological change appears to be somewhat less when non-coal machines of the 1951–53 vintage are compared with non-coal machines of the 1925–29 vintage. But this difference is at most 7.8 points in terms of the index (for the 100 MW machines).

It should be noted that there is a certain amount of extrapolation in these tables beyond the range of machines in each of the cells of table D.6.

Conclusions

If the analysis carried out in this appendix is compared with that of chapter 5 it is seen that there is a pay-off between a somewhat more correct measure of capacity utilisation and a smaller sample.[1] We have seen that the results obtained here do not seriously violate those of chapter 5 and the analysis of technological change and economies of scale for both the sample of chapter 5 and the one-machine plants is very similar.

---

[1] It must be remembered that the one-machine sample is a subset of the total sample used in chapter 5 so that the underestimation of capacity utilisation does not apply to the total sample o chapter 5.

BIBLIOGRAPHY[1]

Books

IULO, WILLIAM, *Electric Utilities – Costs and Performance*. Pullman: Washington State University Press, 1961.

JOHNSTON, J., *Statistical Cost Analysis*. New York: McGraw-Hill Book Company, 1960.

—, *Econometric Methods*. New York: McGraw-Hill Book Company, 1963.

KUH, EDWIN, *Capital Stock Growth: A Micro-Econometric Approach*. Amsterdam: North-Holland Publishing Company, 1963.

LING, SUILIN, *Economies of Scale in the Steam-Electric Power Generating Industry*. Amsterdam: North-Holland Publishing Company, 1964.

MARRIS, ROBIN, *The Economics of Capital Utilisation*. Cambridge: Cambridge University Press, 1964.

Articles in Journals

BARZEL, YORAM, The Production Function and Technical Change in the Steam-Power Industry, *The Journal of Political Economy*, vol. 72, April 1964, pp. 133–150.

CHENERY, HOLLIS B., Overcapacity and the Acceleration Principle, *Econometrica*, vol. 20, January 1952, pp. 1–28.

DHRYMES, PHOEBUS, J., and KURZ, MORDECAI, Technology and Scale in Electricity Generation, *Econometrica*, vol. 32, July 1964, pp. 287–315.

JOHANSEN, LEIF, Substitution Versus Fixed Proportion Coefficients in the Theory of Economic Growth: A Synthesis, *Econometrica*, vol. 27, April 1959, pp. 157–176.

KOMIYA, RYUTARO, Technical Progress and the Production Function in the United States Steam Power Industry, *The Review of Economics and Statistics*, vol. 44, May 1962, pp. 156–166.

KURZ, MORDECAI. *See* Dhrymes.

LOMAX, K. S., Cost Curves for Electricity Generation, *Economica*, New Series, vol. 19, May 1952, pp. 193–197.

NORDIN, J. A., Note on a Light Plant's Cost Curves, *Econometrica*, vol. 15, July 1947, pp. 231–235.

SAMUELSON, PAUL A., Parable and Realism in Capital Theory: The Surrogate Produc-

---

[1] Only works referred to in the text are recorded here.

tion Function, *The Review of Economic Studies*, vol. 29 (3), June 1962, pp. 193–206.
SOLOW, ROBERT M., Substitution and Fixed Proportions in the Theory of Capital, *The Review of Economic Studies*, vol. 29 (3), June 1962, pp. 207–218.

Articles in Collections

MUNDLAK, YAIR, Estimation of Production and Behavioral Functions from a Combination of Cross-Section and Time-Series Data, in: *Measurement in Economics – Studies in Mathematical Economics and Econometrics in Memory of Yehuda Grunfeld*. Stanford: Stanford University Press, 1963, pp. 138–166.
NERLOVE, MARC, Returns to Scale in Electricity Supply, in: *Measurement in Economics – Studies in Mathematical Economics and Econometrics in Memory of Yehuda Grunfeld*. Stanford: Stanford University Press, 1963, pp. 167–198.

Government Publications

Federal Power Commission, *Steam-Electric Plant Construction Cost and Annual Production Expenses 1938–1947*. Washington: Government Printing Office, 1949.
—, *Steam-Electric Plant Construction Cost and Annual Production Expenses*, annually 1948 to 1963. Washington: Government Printing Office.
—, *National Power Survey: 1964*, parts I and II. Washington: Government Printing Office, 1964.
U.S. Bureau of the Census, *Historical Statistics of the United States, Colonial Times to 1957*. Washington: Government Printing Office, 1960.